THE DRAG
OF DO

CW00409371

E.D.V. Prendergast

With contributions from
Dr N.W. Moore
Dr E.A. Jarzembowski

Maps prepared by the Dorset Environmental Records Centre

Dorset Natural History and Archaeological Society
1991

Published by The Dorset Natural History and Archaeological Society,
Dorset County Museum, Dorchester, Dorset DT1 1XA

Printed by: Sherrens, Unit 1 & 2, South Park, Avon Close, Granby Industrial Estate,
Weymouth, Dorset DT4 9YX

British Library Cataloguing-in-Publication Data
Prendergast, E.D.V.
The dragonflies of Dorset.
I. Title
595.733094233

ISBN 0900341327

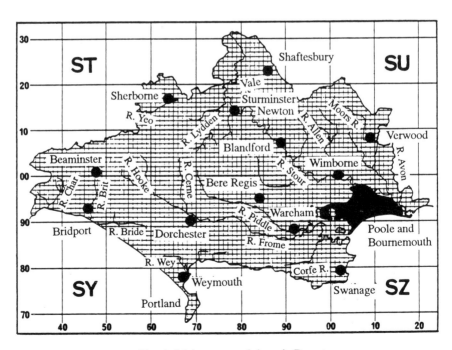

Map 1. Main towns and rivers in Dorset.

CONTENTS

PREFACE

Dorset is a notable county for dragonflies, comparable in richness of breeding species with any in the British Isles. Amongst the 28 are such national rarities as the Small Red, Scarce Blue-tailed and Southern Damselflies, as well as the Scarce Chaser, one of whose national strongholds is in the southern stretches of some of Dorset's rivers.

The considerable upsurge in interest in dragonflies during the last decade has resulted in a great increase in the number of location reports that the Dorset Environmental Records Centre has received. The main aim of this book is to publish these records, together with those concerning the county from the national Biological Records Centre, in the form of distribution maps. These maps will be of interest, primarily, to those who have already some knowledge of these attractive insects and will, it is hoped, result in efforts to fill in some of the gaps that exist on the maps, and to confirm the pre-1980 records.

At the same time, the opportunity has been taken to produce an account of dragonflies in general, and those of Dorset in particular, in sufficient detail to act as an introduction for those with little, or no, previous knowledge. The species accounts, together with the plates, should be sufficient to enable adult dragonflies to be identified. For those who wish to pursue their studies further, a list of recommended books, many with coloured illustrations, is included under the heading of Further Reading on page 70. Dr Norman Moore, one of the foremost authorities in the country, who has a long and continuing association with Dorset, has contributed the introductory chapter on the dragonflies of the present era; and Dr Ed. Jarzembowski the account of their predecessors that lived in Dorset in the age of the dinosaurs, 150 to 200 million years ago.

Dragonflies (Odonata) comprise both Zygoptera (damselflies) and Anisoptera (dragon-flies). To avoid confusion, the latter are spelt with a hyphen in this book.

The Dorset Environmental Records Centre at the County Hall, Dorchester, will be glad to receive records of any sightings of dragonflies in the county and, especially, evidence of breeding. The British Dragonfly Society is concerned with the study and conservation of dragonflies throughout the British Isles, and has a worldwide membership. Details may be obtained from the secretary, Mrs R.I. Silsby, 1 Haydn Avenue, Purley, Surrey CR8 4AG.

It is perhaps fortunate for dragonflies that they are unsatisfactory insects to collect and exhibit in display cases. The beautiful lifetime hues soon fade after death into flat dull colours, unless subjected to freeze-drying or other complicated processes. On the other hand, they are excellent subjects for photography, where their natural colours can be readily recorded on film. For those who desire to collect dragonflies for scientific or other purposes, the British Dragonfly Society has drawn up a Code of Practice which is reproduced, by permission, in Chapter 3. It is hoped that everyone will conform to this Code of Practice and, in particular, to para 5 that 'Permission should always be sought from the landowner or occupier when collecting (or studying) on private land.' Anyone who has watched the exciting aerial manoeuvres of a pair of Hobbies capturing dragonflies, at a rate of more than one per minute, over a heathland pond in order to feed their young, or a party of swallows picking up damselflies along a river or stream, will realise that the effect of responsible collecting by humans is, by comparison, infinitesimal.

Breeding Species

Damselflies	Zygoptera
Beautiful Demoiselle	*Calopteryx virgo* (L)
Banded Demoiselle	*Calopteryx splendens* (Harris)
Emerald Damselfly	*Lestes sponsa* (Hansemann)
White-legged Damselfly	*Platycnemis pennipes* (Pallas)
Large Red Damselfly	*Pyrrhosoma nymphula* (Sulzer)
Small Red Damselfly	*Ceriagrion tenellum* (Villers)
Blue-tailed Damselfly	*Ischnura elegans* (Vander Linden)
Scarce Blue-tailed Damselfly	*Ischnura pumilio* (Charpentier)
Common Blue Damselfly	*Enallagma cyathigerum* (Charpentier)
Azure Damselfly	*Coenagrion puella* (L)
Southern Damselfly	*Coenagrion mercuriale* (Charpentier)
Red-eyed Damselfly	*Erythromma najas* (Hansemann)

Dragon-flies	**Anisoptera**
Hairy Dragon-fly	*Brachytron pratense* (Müller)
Common Hawker	*Aeshna juncea* (L)
Southern Hawker	*Aeshna cyanea* (Müller)
Brown Hawker	*Aeshna grandis* (L)
Migrant Hawker	*Aeshna mixta* (Latreille)
Emperor Dragon-fly	*Anax imperator* (Leach)
Golden-ringed Dragon-fly	*Cordulegaster boltoni* (Donovan)
Downy Emerald	*Cordulia aenea* (L)
Four-spotted Chaser	*Libellula quadrimaculata* (L)
Broad-bodied Chaser	*Libellula depressa* (L)
Scarce Chaser	*Libellula fulva* (Müller)
Black-tailed Skimmer	*Orthetrum cancellatum* (L)
Keeled Skimmer	*Orthetrum coerulescens* (Fabricius)
Common Darter	*Sympetrum striolatum* (Charpentier)
Ruddy Darter	*Sympetrum sanguineum* (Müller)
Black Darter	*Sympetrum danae* (Sulzer)

Vagrants

Vagrant Emperor Dragon-fly	*Hemianax ephippiger* (Burmeister)
Yellow-winged Darter	*Sympetrum flaveolum* (L)
Red-veined Darter	*Sympetrum fonscolombei* (Selys)

No recent Records

Variable Damselfly	*Coenagrion pulchellum* (Vander Linden)
Orange-spotted Emerald	*Oxygastra curtisi* (Dale)
Club-tailed Dragon-fly	*Gomphus vulgatissimus* (L)

Table 1. List of Dorset Dragonflies (Odonata)

Chapter 1 - DRAGONFLIES - UNUSUAL INSECTS

by N.W. Moore

Dragonflies are very unusual insects. They are survivors from the distant past: there were dragonflies before there were any dinosaurs. They were flying above the swamps and forests of giant horsetails long before the appearance of mammals, birds, flowering plants and insects like butterflies, beetles and bees. Today dragonflies form an isolated group of animals. Their wings, and the way they are attached to the body, show that mayflies are their nearest surviving relations.

Dragonflies are like all insects in being segmented (Fig 1), and in possessing an exoskeleton made mainly of chitin. The head is formed from six segments, of which four carry appendages - the antennae, and the mandibles, maxillae and labium which form the mouth parts. Each of the three segments of the thorax carries legs, and in the adult the second and third segments, which are fused together, support wings. The possession of an exoskeleton means that, as dragonflies grow, they have to shed their skins and grow new ones. Like all other insects, they respire by means of long elastic tubes called tracheae. In the adults these connect with the outside world by means of openings called spiracles. Dragonflies have a pair of well-developed compound eyes and three simple eyes called ocelli.

Some dragonflies are bigger than some mammals and birds but none is very large, and the largest ones flying today are much smaller than the giant primitive dragonflies which

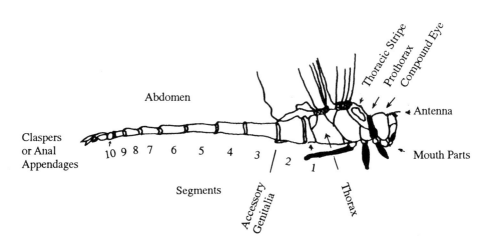

Figure 1. Structure of adult dragonfly.

were about in the Carboniferous period. The nature of the exoskeleton, and the limitations in fuel supply to the flight muscles, make it impossible to have very large insects. However, it is not obvious why no living dragonfly approaches the size of the Carboniferous dragonflies with their two-foot wingspan. Perhaps in a world with no birds or bats, it was easier for large slow-flying insects to survive.

The more recently evolved insects like beetles, butterflies and bees go through a resting, pupal stage in which the larva is transformed into an adult. This allows for great differences between larva and adult. However dragonflies, like mayflies, stoneflies, earwigs and grasshoppers, do not have a pupa. The developing wings become external in the later larval instars. As with all insects, the time spent as a larva is relatively lengthy, the latter's functions being feeding and growing. The adult dragonfly continues to feed but its main function is to reproduce its kind.

Dragonflies, like mayflies and stoneflies, are terrestrial animals which have aquatic larva. Dispersal to new habitats is achieved by adults. Dragonflies are particularly good dispersers, quickly discovering new waters provided by nature or by man.

Dragonflies have a number of unique features not found in other insects. For example, most other insects move their wings by contracting and relaxing the muscles of the thorax: this levers the wings up and down. In dragonflies the main flight muscles are attached to the wings themselves; in this they resemble birds and bats rather than insects. Dragonflies excel in their flying abilities; they can fly very fast and have great powers of manoeuvre. Their wings are large, tough, light and flexible. Unlike butterflies and many other insects, the fore and hind wings are not connected with each other. In fact, in most species the fore and hind wings always beat out of phase. Dragonflies usually have a noticeable wing spot, or 'pterostigma', near the end of the leading edge of each wing, as well as a change of alignment in the leading edge of each wing, known as the nodus (p. 8). These features, combined with the independence of the wings, probably contribute to the great manoeuvrability which is such a feature of dragonflies, and which makes the large ones so difficult to catch.

One of the great mysteries about dragonflies is why they mate in the way they do. Before mating, the male transfers his sperm from the ninth abdominal segment to complicated genitalia on the underside of the second and third segments. This apparatus is unique to dragonflies. When the male has caught a female, he seizes her head (in dragon-flies) or the front of her thorax (in damselflies). She then bends her abdomen round to receive the sperm in her spermatheca in her eighth abdominal segment. One often sees dragonflies in this 'wheel formation' in the field (p. 8). Recently, it has been discovered that parts of the accessory genitalia of some male dragonflies are used to get rid of any sperm that may remain in the spermatheca of the female from a previous mating. When this sperm has been removed, the male replaces it with his own. Other insects have ways of giving their own sperm a better chance of being used, but it appears that only dragonflies have special instruments on the penis to remove sperm left over from previous matings.

Dragonflies are unique among insects in using their heads as balancing organs. When the insect moves from the horizontal, the inertia of the head relative to the body is picked up by sense organs in the very narrow neck. If a dragonfly is caught in a net this delicate mechanism is often damaged by the sudden blow, and its ability to fly may be impaired or totally lost. The ocelli are also involved with orientating the dragonfly in space.

Dragonfly larvae also have unique features (Fig 2). Like the adult, the larva is a predator. It waits for its prey or stalks it and, when it is in range, it shoots out its lower lip or labium, whose hooks impale the prey. The extension of the labium is achieved through hydrostatic pressure which is built up in the abdomen.

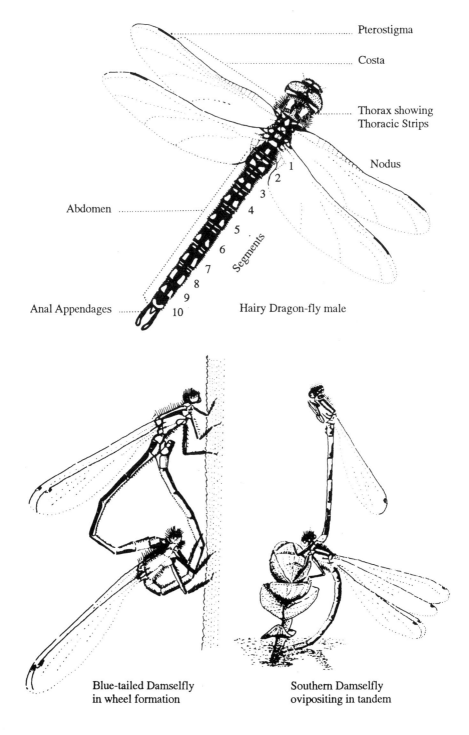

Pterostigma

Costa

Thorax showing
Thoracic Strips

Nodus

1
2
3
4
5
6
7
8
9
10

Segments

Abdomen

Anal Appendages

Hairy Dragon-fly male

Blue-tailed Damselfly
in wheel formation

Southern Damselfly
ovipositing in tandem

Damselfly larvae have conspicuous external gills at the end of the abdomen, but dragon-fly larvae have their gills in the rectum, and water is pumped in and out in order to supply the necessary oxygen. Dragon-fly larvae can use this pumping action as an escape mechanism; if a larva is in danger, it can save itself by jet propulsion.

All in all, dragonflies are strange creatures which differ markedly from other insects.

The Natural History of Dragonflies

Many years ago I called dragonflies 'The Birdwatcher's Insect' because they were so large that they could be watched with binoculars in the field like birds (Corbet, Longfield and Moore, 1960). Often one can get so close to dragonflies that a monocular has to be used; when dragonfly watching, it is best to carry both instruments. It is the size of dragonflies which makes them a marvellous group to study. Many can be identified in the field without having to catch them. We can identify individual insects by noting peculiarities, or by marking them distinctively with cellulose paint or a felt pen. We can watch how they spend their day in great detail.

It is important to understand the basic natural history of dragonflies if we are to get to know them at all, because we can easily miss them if we do not know how they react to the seasons, weather and the time of day. It is possible to visit a place teeming with dragonflies and not see any if we do not know when and where to look for them.

Two things dominate the life of adult dragonflies - sun and water. They are essentially tropical animals and must make use of the warmest times of the year and day, and they need water in which to breed.

While adult dragonflies are familiar to most people, their larvae are not, as they are

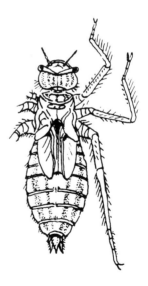

Figure 2. Larva of damselfly (left) and of dragon-fly.

9

inconspicuously coloured and live hidden in water-weed or in mud below the water surface. However, they are easily found by dipping a net into unpolluted ponds, slowly moving streams and rivers.

In the course of their development, dragonflies go through a varying number of moults (6 to 15). The first larval instar, known as a prolarva, has no free legs and exists for only a few seconds or hours after hatching from the egg. The second instar is an active little creature, fully equipped with legs and compound eyes, and uses its tiny labium to catch minute prey. The external wing buds do not appear until later instars. The rate of larval development depends on temperature. In Britain, species usually take one or two years, although individuals of some take three. Low environmental temperatures prevent development, so dragonflies go into a stage of suspended development, or diapause, during the winter. In some species, such as the Emerald Damselfly (*Lestes sponsa*), diapause occurs in the egg stage, but in others like the Emperor Dragon-fly (*Anax imperator*) it occurs in the final larval instar. No British dragonfly hibernates as an adult, but the Winter Damselfly (*Sympecma fusca*), a relation of the Emerald Damselfly, does so on the other side of the English Channel. Species which go through diapause in the last larval instar emerge at approximately the same time in the earlier part of the year, and so are called spring species. Mass emergence ensures that they find mates easily; and there is safety in numbers as far as predators are concerned. However, if mass emergence coincides with bad weather many insects may die. Spring species include common ones like the Large Red Damselfly (*Pyrrhosoma nymphula*), Four-spotted Chaser (*Libellula quadrimaculata*) and the Emperor Dragon-fly, and rarer ones like the Hairy Dragon-fly (*Brachytron pratense*) and Downy Emerald (*Cordulia aenea*).

Damselfly larvae and hawker (*Aeshnidae*) larvae are long and thin: other dragon-flies have more squat bodies. The larvae of the Golden-ringed Dragon-fly (*Cordulegaster boltoni*) bury themselves in the mud or sand of small stream beds, those of the Four-spotted Chaser and Black-tailed Skimmer (*Orthetrum cancellatum*) in mud and debris of ponds and dykes, and the Downy Emerald in rotting vegetation. The larvae of the Beautiful Demoiselle (*Calopteryx virgo*) hold fast to water-weeds, and wait for food to come within striking distance. In the earlier stages, all larvae use their antennae to locate food. The Beautiful Demoiselle uses this method throughout its larval life, whereas the Downy Emerald uses a mixture of sense organs. The later stages of the Emerald Damselfly and hawker larvae actively seek out their prey using their well developed eyes.

The colour of some larvae varies according to age and, in some cases, to background. The early instars of hawker larvae have a banded pattern not found in later stages. Recently it has been shown that the larvae of some damselflies, including the Large Red Damselfly, are territorial.

The transformation of the dragonfly larva into an adult is one of the great sights of nature. The drama is often missed because it frequently occurs at night or in the early morning. The actual time of emergence is controlled by day length and temperature. When it emerges, the larva climbs up a rush or some other water plant growing in, or by, the water. In some species it may crawl for quite a distance from the water before making its metamorphosis. After great exertions, the adult dragonfly finally breaks through its larval skin and perches on it. This empty larval skin will remain on the plant until washed away by rain or blown away by wind. The discarded skins of the last larval instars are known as exuviae. Their presence provides absolute proof that the species concerned actually bred at that particular water. This information is very important, because adult dragonflies often hold territories by water which is unsuitable for them; in other words seeing an adult by a pond is not proof that it is breeding there, but finding an exuvia is.

The wings of the newly-emerged dragonfly expand quickly and harden. The soft pale brown 'teneral' insect then flies away from the water in order to avoid the attentions of its kind, and of predators assembled at the water's edge. For several days it lives in the fields and woods as an immature adult. At such times dragonflies are less colourful and, in some species, males tend to look like females. When the insect's cuticle has hardened and its gonads have developed, it begins to visit water - males to set up territories, find females and mate with them, and females to find males, mate and lay eggs.

Most, but not all, dragonflies are territorial to some degree. Some defend particular stretches of water, while others are merely aggressive where they happen to be. Hawker dragon-flies guard their territories by flying up and down the edge of the pond or river; others perch on the ground nearby (eg Black-tailed Skimmer), or perch on water plants (eg Scarce Chaser (*Libellula fulva*) and make occasional sallies of inspection. The size of territories varies with the size of the insect. That is why a small garden pond can never hold more than one male Southern Hawker (*Aeshna cyanea*), or Broad-bodied Chaser (*Libellula depressa*), but may have several Blue-tailed Damselflies (*Ischnura elegans*). Studies on dragonfly territories show that, for each species, there is a population density (the 'highest steady density', measured as the number of males per 100m of water edge) which is rarely exceeded. The total population depends on the length of unshaded water edge available and the insects' behaviour. This means that, once you know the length of a pond's edge and the 'highest steady density' of the species, you can predict the maximum number of territories of the species which the pond is likely to support.

Damselflies and hawker dragon-flies lay elongated eggs which they insert into aquatic plants or into vegetation at the water's edge. Other dragon-flies place their sticky eggs on water-weeds, while still others broadcast them while flying over the water. Ruddy Darters (*Sympetrum sanguineum*) can often be seen dropping their eggs onto marshy ground several inches away from the water's edge. Eggs which are stuck to water-weed, or are dropped into water, are rounded in shape. Females may lay eggs on their own, or accompanied by the male. Both types of behaviour can occur in the same species. In species which lay eggs in plants, the males often continue to hold the female by the claspers at the end of their abdomen (p. 8) even when the female is completely submerged in water. This behaviour prevents other males from attempting to mate with the ovipositing female, and hence disturbing the eggs which they have fertilised. It may also help the female to get away quickly if threatened by a predator above or below the water. The male Common Darter (*Sympetrum striolatum*) often remains attached to the female in the 'tandem' position, while the female scatters eggs on the surface of the water. In other species, for example Four-spotted Chaser, the male separates from the female but usually hovers just above her on guard as she lays eggs. This enables him to chase off other males attempting to mate with the female, but leaves him free to mate with other females if they appear. Females of several species have a posture indicating that they are unwilling to mate.

Male dragonflies only set up territories when it is warm enough; in other words, they only go to the water when it is a fine day, and only from mid-morning until late afternoon. Females go to water for a much shorter time - only to mate and lay eggs. Therefore if you visit a pond it always appears that there are many more males than females. In fact the sex ratio is nearly 50:50 but, at any one moment, most of the females are feeding away from the water and are much less readily seen.

Mating takes only a few seconds in some species (eg Four-spotted Chaser); in others the pair may leave the water and hang up in the branches of a tree where the process may take over an hour (eg Common Hawker (*Aeshna juncea*), Blue-tailed Damselfly and Emerald Damselfly).

Some feeding is done by water, but it mainly occurs away from it in nearby woods and fields. During the night, and in bad weather, dragonflies roost in trees or bushes, or perch on grasses or other plants. Dragon-flies generally roost some way from water but damselflies fairly near it, and in some cases even on the rushes and sedges at the water's edge. They are very inconspicuous at such times, and damselflies often make themselves more so by sidling round the stem on which they perch, so that the stem is between them and the observer. When they get up in the morning, dragonflies often have to 'rev up' by beating their wings in order to raise their body temperature so that they can fly.

Territorial behaviour can lead to dispersal of ousted males, but most dispersal appears to take place at the time of the maiden flight away from the water when the adult is immature.

Each species has its own particular pattern of behaviour. There is much to be discovered about the daily life of even our commonest species.

In a short review of this kind, generalisations have to be made without qualification. The reader should be warned that there are exceptions to nearly every rule, and they are often of very great interest.

For an up-to-date and fuller summary of dragonfly biology, the reader is referred to Peter Miller's excellent *Dragonflies*, Naturalists' Handbook 7, Cambridge University Press, and to Philip Corbet's classic *Biology of Dragonflies*.

Dragonflies in Dorset

The distribution of dragonflies in Dorset is largely determined by the county's geology, the rate of flow of its rivers and streams, and by human activities past and present.

Much of Dorset consists of chalk and Jurassic limestone (Map 2). These strata are porous

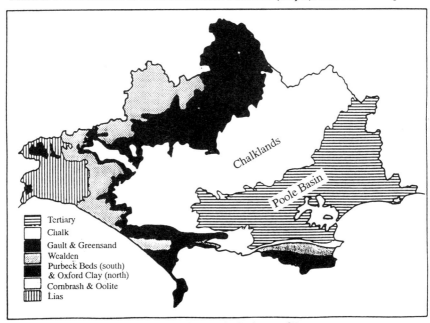

Map 2. Simplified geological map of Dorset.

and support no natural permanent waters, and so the districts where they occur are poor in dragonflies. In other areas, many of the rivers and streams are too fast for British dragonflies. In other parts of the world many species of dragonflies are adapted to living in fast rivers, streams and waterfalls, but none of these species occurs in the British Isles.

Little Sea on Studland Heath is one of the very few natural lakes in southern England. It, and the numerous bog pools on the Tertiary Beds of the Poole Basin, provide exceptionally good habitats for dragonflies, and a glance at the distribution maps shows the extent to which dragonflies favour this part of Dorset. The Poole Basin covers about 28% of the county, the chalklands 32% and the remainder, loosely termed the vales, some 40%.

Man has destroyed or damaged breeding areas of dragonflies in Dorset through industrial and agricultural pollution, but he has also greatly supported dragonflies, both through mineral workings and through farming activities. He has made good the lack of natural waters by creating cattle ponds, duck decoys, ornamental lakes, thousands of garden ponds, and by digging numerous ditches which hold water throughout the year. In the heathland areas of the Poole Basin, the natural habitats are supported and outnumbered by water-filled clay pits and shell holes derived from military training, and by bomb holes provided by the Luftwaffe.

Laurie Friday (Barnes, 1983; Friday, 1987 and 1988), in her studies of the Purbeck clay pits, has shown how important these are for dragonflies, and how they get better for dragonflies as the years go by. In the 1950s, I used bomb holes in the Arne peninsula to carry out field experiments on populations of different species of dragonflies. By adding or subtracting males, I was able to determine the highest steady densities of the different species studied. The wealth of species present enabled me to study some aspects of interspecific competition (Moore, 1964). If it were not for ponds deliberately or accidentally made by man, dragonflies would be far less numerous in Dorset today. The British Dragonfly Society has published an excellent paper on Pond Construction for Dragonflies, which is reproduced, by permission, as Chapter 5.

In Dorset, three species depend on unpolluted rivers with a moderate flow, although all occasionally breed in lakes or ponds. They are the Banded Demoiselle (*Calopteryx splendens*), the White-legged Damselfly (*Platycnemis pennipes*) and the Scarce Chaser. The Beautiful Demoiselle breeds in smaller, faster streams usually lined by trees. The Golden-ringed Dragon-fly breeds in shallow streams, and the Southern Damselfly (*Coenagrion mercuriale*) in gently flowing seepages in bogs. The Small Red Damselfly (*Ceriagrion tenellum*), the Scarce Blue-tailed Damselfly (*Ischnura pumilio*), the Southern Damselfly, Common Hawker, Keeled Skimmer (*Orthetrum coerulescens*) and Black Darter (*Sympetrum danae*) are virtually confined to acid bogs and streams in the Poole Basin; elsewhere, especially on the Continent, the Scarce Blue-tailed Damselfly also occurs in base-rich waters. The Ruddy Darter requires marshy places with a higher pH. Ten of the Dorset species are very catholic in their requirements and occur widely throughout the County. The Brown Hawker (*Aeshna grandis*), Red-eyed Damselfly (*Erythromma najas*) and Variable Damselfly (*Coenagrion pulchellum*) are rarer than might be expected; indeed there are no recent accepted records for the last.

Very sadly, Dorset's most interesting species, the Orange-spotted Emerald (*Oxygastra curtisi*) is extinct. The species was first discovered by Mr J.C. Dale on Parley Heath, near the present Hurn airport, on June 29th 1820. He described it as a new species in Loudon's Magazine in 1834. It bred on the Moors River and survived there until about 1962 when it was apparently exterminated by pollution of the river by sewage. There are also records from Devonshire, the latest in 1946. It can never have been common as the amount of available habitat was small; in 1957 I estimated that a third of its range in Dorset could only support six territories. The Orange-spotted Emerald has one of the most restricted ranges of any European dragonfly, and it has disappeared from many localities. Its range extends from the Netherlands and North Italy to Northern Spain and Portugal. Fortunately it is still common in parts of France and Spain.

Another Dorset speciality is the Scarce Chaser, which has a patchy distribution in England and the Continent. It occurs on the Stour, Moors River and the Frome. Dorset is one of its strongholds in Britain. Its survival will depend on keeping these rivers free from pollution. The Southern Damselfly, Scarce Blue-tailed Damselfly and Small Red Damselfly are very local in Britain and are vulnerable to heathland reclamation. The Poole Basin heaths and the New Forest are strongholds of these species in Britain. The Southern Damselfly is an endangered species in several European countries.

Dragonflies in Context

There are very approximately the same number of species of dragonfly in the world as there are birds - certainly 5,000 but probably less than 10,000. Whereas most birds have been described, many dragonflies await discovery. The vast majority of species live in the tropical rain-forests, notably those of South America and Southeast Asia. However, many species occur in temperate regions and some are very numerous. Some, including the Common Blue Damselfly (*Enallagma cyathigerum*), even occur north of the Arctic Circle.

Like most islands, Britain has a relatively impoverished fauna compared with that of its neighbouring continent. Of 114 species which occur in Europe, only 39 breed in the British Isles, and one of these, the recently discovered Irish Damselfly (*Coenagrion lunulatum*), only occurs in Ireland. In addition, four other species, Red-veined Darter (*Sympetrum fonscolombei*) Yellow-winged Darter (*Sympetrum flaveolum*), Vagrant Darter (*Sympetrum vulgatum*) and Vagrant Emperor Dragon-fly (*Hemianax ephippiger*) visit our shores from time to time but do not maintain permanent breeding populations here. They are the dragonfly equivalents of Red Admiral and Clouded Yellow Butterflies. The Migrant Hawker (*Aeshna mixta*) and Common and Ruddy Darters occur both as migrants and as residents.

Although 34 species have been recorded in Dorset, only 28 now breed in the County. Of those which once bred, the Orange-spotted Emerald is now extinct in Britain, and there have been no recent breeding records of the Variable Damselfly or the Red-veined Darter. The Club-tailed Dragon-fly (*Gomphus vulgatissimus*) probably only visited Dorset from the New Forest, while the Yellow-winged Darter is an infrequent visitor from the Continent, and the Vagrant Emperor Dragon-fly has occurred just once. The Dorset dragonfly fauna is very similar to that of the neighbouring county of Hampshire, which additionally has the Brilliant Emerald (*Somatochlora metallica*). Dorset and Hampshire owe their abundance of dragonflies to their relatively warm climate, and to the presence of lowland heath with its bogs.

It is interesting to consider where Dorset dragonflies occur outside Britain. All are found elsewhere in continental Europe; Banded Demoiselle, Orange-spotted Emerald and Keeled Skimmer are confined to Europe. The Southern Damselfly, Small Red Damselfly, Migrant Hawker, Black-tailed Skimmer and Common Darter are essentially Mediterranean species and occur in North Africa as well as Europe. The Common Hawker and Black Darter are characteristic of Northern Europe. Twenty-four of the Dorset species occur in Northern Asia, although five of them only get as far as the Near East. One can see Common Hawkers, Migrant Hawkers, Downy Emerald, Four-spotted Chasers and Black Darters in

Japan. Common Blue Damselflies, Common Hawkers, Four-spotted Chasers and Black Darters occur in North America as well as Northern Asia. The only breeding species Dorset shares with tropical Africa is the splendid Emperor Dragon-fly. It occurs as far south as the Cape, also in Madagascar and parts of the Near East. The Red-veined Darter is a visitor from Africa and Europe, while the Yellow-winged Darter comes to us from Europe and Asia.

Dragonflies have tremendous powers of dispersal and therefore we should always keep an eye out for species which have not yet been recorded from Dorset. No fewer than twelve species never seen in Dorset breed in France, just the other side of the English Channel. Climatic change may change the dragonfly fauna of Dorset in the future.

Figure 3. Banded Demoiselle, *Calopteryx splendens.*

15

CHAPTER 2. SPECIES ACCOUNTS AND DISTRIBUTION

In the following accounts, the dragonflies occurring in Dorset are mainly grouped in pairs, often of similar species. The text accompanying the distribution maps and plates contains short descriptions which draw attention, where applicable, to the differences between the two species and other similar species, notes on habitat, abundance and distribution in the County in particular and Britain as a whole. For reasons of space, the descriptions are chiefly of mature adults, which have stronger colours and are often more easily recognizable than the newly emerged insects. The colours of the latter change gradually as the insects develop from the teneral stage to the mature adult. For descriptions of all the life cycle stages one of the more comprehensive publications listed on page 70 should be consulted.

The distribution maps have been plotted by 1 km grid squares for each species. These maps have been prepared by the Dorset Environmental Records Centre from the reports of local recorders, and from the records of the Biological Records Centre of the Institute of Terrestrial Ecology. Records from before 1970 are shown by a diagonal line, those from 1970 to 1979 by a halved square and those from 1980 to August 1991 by a black square. A marked square merely indicates that the species has at least once during the period been

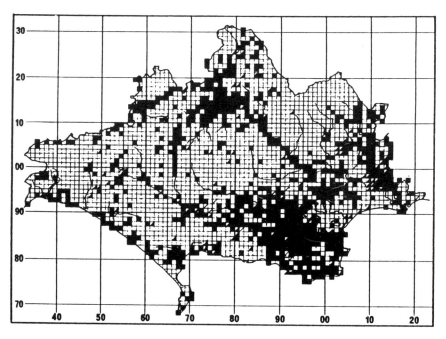

Map 3. All records; 1 km squares for which records have been received. Whilst the north and south-east - the Poole Basin - have been fairly well covered, the west has so far been under-recorded. Not unexpectedly, there are few records from the Chalklands (see Map 2), except from the river valleys.

recorded there, and is no indication of its abundance within the square: indeed it may not even breed in the square. The limits of the Poole Basin, the stronghold of some species, is shown on the relevant maps. Map 3 shows the 1 km squares within the County for which records have been received; and Map 4 the number of species which have been reported in each 10 km square. Though some records have been rejected by the DERC for a variety of reasons, there is still some doubt about certain others submitted prior to 1980. These latter records have been retained for individual species maps but, where they are the only records for a 10 km square, they have been omitted from the totals on Map 4. It should be appreciated that the apparent absence of a species from a square does not necessarily mean that it does not occur there. It may merely indicate that the square has not been visited by a recorder. However, though, doubtless species will be added to some of the 10 km squares, the overall pattern shown on Map 4 - with the highest number of species being found in the Poole Basin, and the lowest in the chalklands - is unlikely to change.

Knowledge of the time of year at which the various species are on the wing is a useful aid to identification. The approximate period during which each species may be expected to be found in Dorset is shown in Table 2. The date of emergence is influenced by a number of factors, the most important of which is temperature. Thus it can be appreciated that the peak period along the Purbeck coast is likely to be rather earlier than in, for instance, the Blackmore Vale. Similarly, after a mild winter and warm spring, emergence will

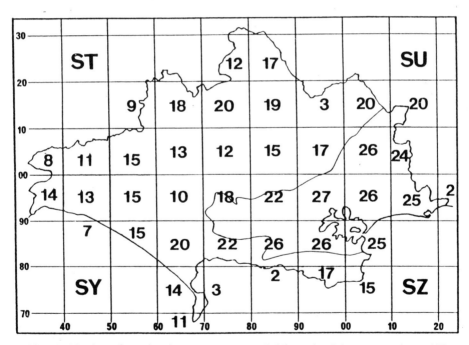

Map 4. Number of species, less vagrants, recorded in each 10 km square since 1970. Nearly all the 28 species that breed in Dorset have been recorded in most of the 10 km squares in the Poole Basin in the south-eastern third of the County. The high numbers in certain squares in the Blackmore Vale in the central north and the lower numbers in the west, are at least partly a reflection of the numbers of observers.

everywhere be earlier than in a year of prolonged cold weather. The total flight period for each species may be considerably longer than the period shown, the earliest hatchings being often two or more weeks beforehand, and insects being still on the wing for a similar time afterwards, with odd individuals surviving even longer under favourable conditions.

Outline guide to male dragonflies. This is a very much simplified guide to adult male insects, which may be useful in directing attention to the appropriate pages of the species accounts. It is only applicable to those species that occur in Dorset.

A. Damselflies - Zygoptera

Page

Slender bodied, feeble fliers. Eyes widely separated. Front and hind wings similar in shape. When settled, wings are held:

a. Half open	- Emerald Damselflies	24
b. Together	- Other damselflies; see below	

Species with coloured wings, shining green abdomen

	- Beautiful Demoiselle	22 &
	- Banded Demoiselle	Fig. 3 (p. 15)

Species with clear wings; abdomen colour mainly;

a. Red	- Large Red Damselfly, Small Red Damselfly	34
b. Dark, tipped with blue		
With dark eyes	-Blue-tailed Damselfly	30
	- Scarce Blue-tailed Damselfly	30
With red eyes	- Red-eyed Damselfly	32

c. Blue, with black markings;		
Common	- Common Blue Damselfly	28
	- Azure Damselfly	28
Purbeck only	- Southern Damselfly	32
No recent records	-Variable Damselfly	28
d. Pale blue, with white legs;		
	- White-legged Damselfly	24

B. Dragon-flies - Anisoptera

Stout bodied, fast flying. Eyes meet at top of head (all Dorset breeding species). Front and hind wings markedly different in shape. When settled, wings held horizontal. Most have clear wings. Generally in descending order of size. Sizes are approximate and given in terms of the average overall length/average wingspan in mm.

19

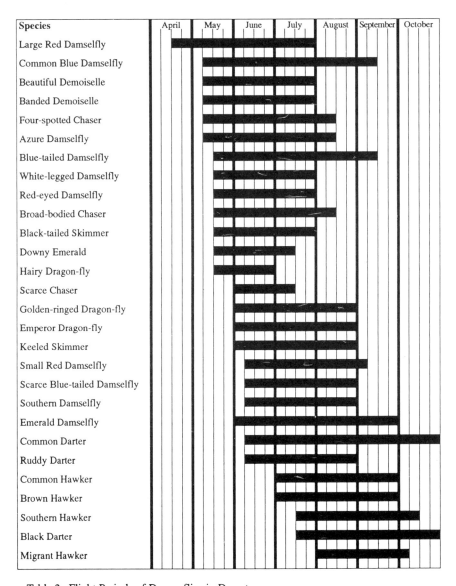

Table 2. Flight Periods of Dragonflies in Dorset

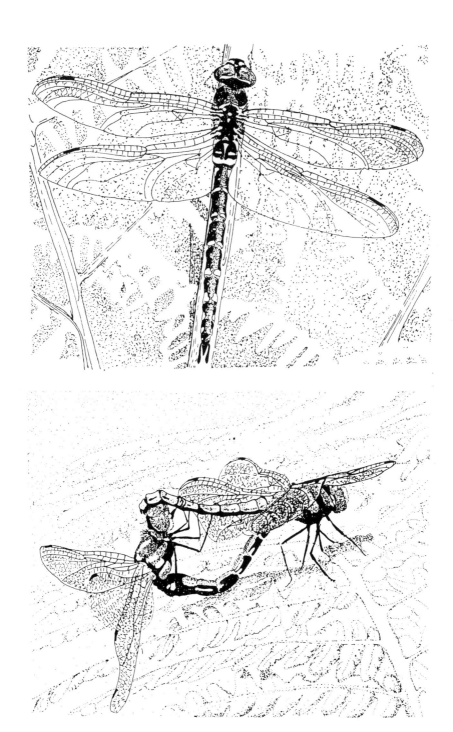

BEAUTIFUL DEMOISELLE
Calopteryx virgo
Map 5

BANDED DEMOISELLE
Calopteryx splendens
Fig. 3 (p. 15) Map 6

These are two of the largest and most beautiful damselflies, quite unlike any other species, with their dancing flight, coloured wings and shining metallic-green thoraxes and abdomens. They are both stream dwellers, but whilst the Beautiful Demoiselle prefers fast, clear, running waters, such as those found in the west and north of the County, the Banded Demoiselle is more at home on the slower running streams with muddy bottoms. In some places both species occur: where this happens, the Banded Demoiselle tends to be more aggressive and the dominant species. The Beautiful Demoiselle tolerates some shading by trees, as long as there are clear patches where the sunlight penetrates; but the Banded Demoiselle demands open meadows on the banks of its haunts, where up to half a dozen males may be seen at times indulging in chases over the surface and along the edges of the water. Both species may occur in large numbers on reaches of favourable streams, the fluttering flight and brilliant bodies of the males standing out in the sunlight, whilst wandering individuals may be found far from their breeding places.

The band on the otherwise clear wings of the male Banded Demoiselle progresses with age from light purple-brown to deep Prussian blue. In contrast, almost the entire wing area of the Beautiful Demoiselle changes from purple brown to deep blue-violet. The females are harder to tell apart. The wings of the Banded Demoiselle tend to be green rather than the russet of those of the Beautiful Demoiselle, which are broader and have a finer pattern of veins.

The Beautiful Demoiselle is found mainly to the south-west of a line between London and Liverpool, with outposts in Cumbria and western Scotland. The Banded Demoiselle is more generally distributed south of a line from Liverpool to the Tees.

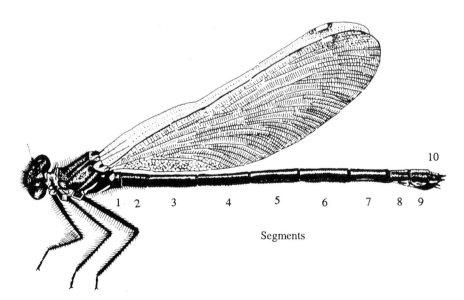

Segments

Beautiful Demoiselle female at 2½ times life size.

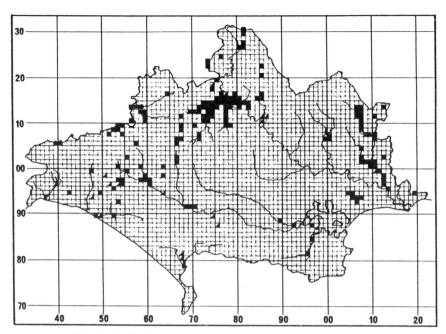

Map 5. Distribution map of Beautiful Demoiselle, *Calopteryx virgo.*

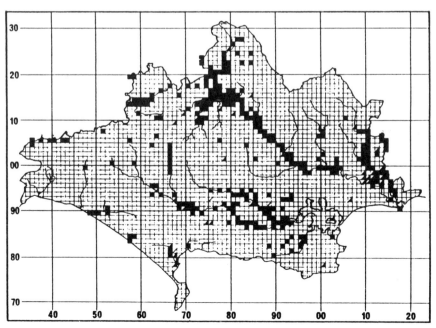

Map 6. Distribution map of Banded Demoiselle, *Calopteryx splendens.*

23

EMERALD DAMSELFLY
Lestes sponsa
Map 7

WHITE-LEGGED DAMSELFLY
Platycnemis pennipes
Map 8 (p. 26)

The Emerald Damselflies characteristically settle with their wings half open, and not closed vertically like other damselflies. Apart from vagrants, two species occur in Britain, the Emerald Damselfly and the similar Scarce Emerald Damselfly (*Lestes dryas*) which was thought to be extinct in Britain until rediscovered in 1983 in East Anglia.

Although robust, the Emerald Damselfly is smaller and more slender than the Demoiselles. It has a metallic green body tinged with bronze. In the male the eyes and the front of the head are pale blue, and the sides of the thorax and the first two and last two abdominal segments develop a pale blue covering - 'pruinescence' - with age. The female remains bronzy green.

The Emerald Damselfly haunts well vegetated ponds and ditches; it flourishes in acidic waters, and is widely distributed throughout the British Isles. In Dorset, it is almost confined to the Poole Basin, with but a few records from elsewhere. It is scarce in the Blackmore Vale, but sometimes numerous at the southern end of Sutton Bingham Reservoir.

The White-legged Damselfly is another distinctive species, the only one with 'white legs'. These are conspicuous, as the hind tibia have feather-like extensions which make the white hind legs appear to be three times broader than those of other species. Both sexes are creamy white on emergence, and may then be found in abundance along hedges and in waterside vegetation near suitable slow-running rivers and streams.

As he matures, the male turns a pale enamel blue with thin dark dorsal markings on the abdomen. The female normally assumes a light green colour with some dark markings. A few females may remain creamy white with only a few dark spots and lines. This form is known as *lactea*.

This species is susceptible to pollution, but this cannot be the sole reason why, in Dorset, it is almost confined to the River Stour and some of its tributaries, mainly in the upper reaches, despite the existence of purer waters elsewhere. Nationally, it is a locally common species in the southern and midland counties but does not occur north of the Wash.

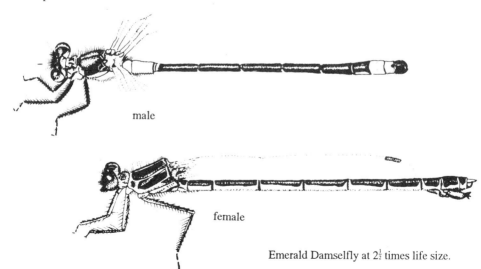

male

female

Emerald Damselfly at $2\frac{1}{2}$ times life size.

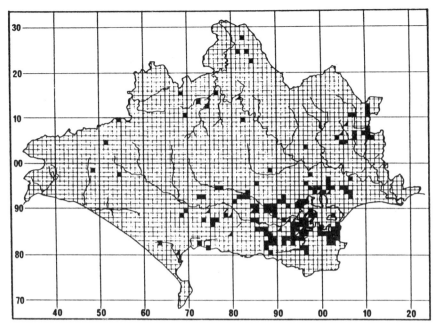

Map 7. Distribution map of Emerald Damselfly, *Lestes sponsa*.

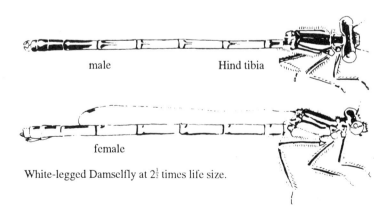

male   Hind tibia

female

White-legged Damselfly at 2¾ times life size.

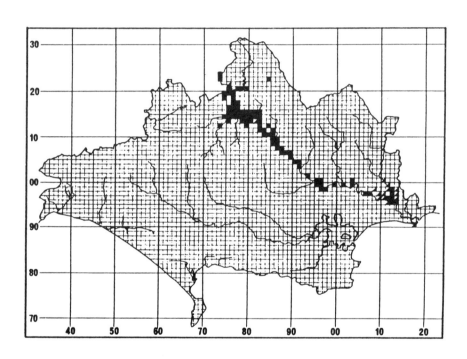

Map 8. Distribution map of White-legged Damselfly, *Platycnemis pennipes.*

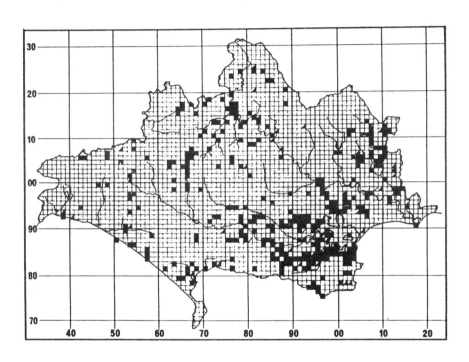

Map 9. Distribution map of Common Blue Damselfly, *Enallagma cyathigerum.*

COMMON BLUE DAMSELFLY
Enallagma cyathigerum
Map 9 (p. 27)

AZURE DAMSELFLY
Coenagrion puella
Map 10

Both of these damselflies are widespread in Britain: the Common Blue occurs throughout, but the Azure does not penetrate far into Scotland. Both species are common in Dorset and gaps on the maps mainly reflect a lack of observers or suitable habitat. The Common Blue Damselfly has a preference for large open ponds with abundant marginal vegetation, whereas the Azure Damselfly is more at home on slow flowing streams and ditches. Nevertheless, both species are found in a wide range of habitats, sometimes occurring in large numbers and frequently together. Newly dug garden or farm ponds are usually soon colonised by one or both species.

The males of the two species are very similar and easily confused. Though both have a blue-striped thorax and a blue abdomen with black markings, there are significant differences which are most easily seen when the insect is perched, and which are clearly shown on the drawing.

	Common Blue	Azure
Thoracic stripes	Broad	Narrow
Segment 2	Black ball with short stalk to joint - occasionally there is no stalk.	Black U, unconnected to joint
Segments 8 & 9	All blue	8 blue; 9 only front part blue; rear part black

The abdomens of the females show considerable colour variation, but are either yellowish-green or bluish with dark markings. One constant character of the female Common Blue is a broad arrow mark on segment 8, which the Azure lacks. Normally there is a 'thistle head' mark on segment 2 in both species, but this is sometimes replaced in the Azure by a thickened 'mercury' sign. This can lead to confusion with the Southern Damselfly *Coenagrion mercuriale*.

The typical Variable Damselfly *Coenagrion pulchellum* - also shown on Plate IV - closely resembles the Azure Damselfly, but, as its name implies, it is very variable and close scrutiny is needed to identify it. The chief distinguishing points are the parallel thoracic stripes, the markings on segment 2 and the deeply indented hind margin of the prothorax. It is sparsely distributed, though locally abundant, in England but quite common in Southern Ireland. There are no recent accepted records for Dorset, but there is no apparent reason why it should not occur in the County.

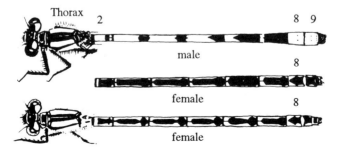

Common Blue Damselfly at $2\frac{1}{2}$ times life size.

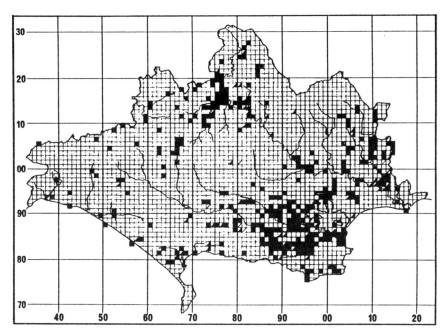

Map 10. Distribution map of Azure Damselfly, *Coenagrion puella.*

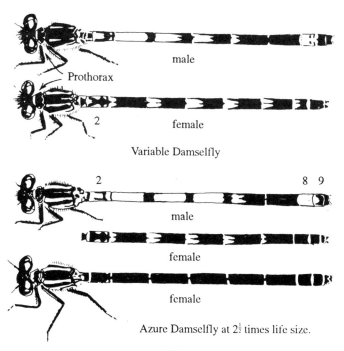

male

Prothorax

2   female

Variable Damselfly

2   8 9

male

female

female

Azure Damselfly at $2\frac{1}{2}$ times life size.

BLUE-TAILED DAMSELFLY
Ischnura elegans
Map 11

SCARCE BLUE-TAILED DAMSELFLY
Ischnura pumilio
Map 12

The Blue-tailed is much sturdier than the Scarce Blue-tailed, which is a delicate insect with a feeble fluttering flight. The males are alike in their colouring. Both have black abdomens except for the final segments, parts of which are blue. The chief differences are the shiny black abdomen of the Blue-tailed in which only segment 8 is blue, whereas in the Scarce Blue-tailed the abdomen is dull black and only part of segment 8, but all of segment 9 normally is blue. The typical female of the Blue-tailed is much like the male. However there are other forms, some of which are not uncommon, in which all of segment 8 is dull brown or blue and the sides of the thorax are violet, olive-green, brown or rose-pink. In one form *infuscans obsoleta* the thorax is brown, with no thoracic stripes and a dull brown band on segment 8. The normal form of the Scarce Blue-tailed female is also similar to the male, but segments 8 and 9 are bronze-black without any blue. One very attractive variety *aurantiaca* has a bright orange thorax and base to the abdomen. It has recently been discovered that this is an immature form which soon changes into a typical adult.

The Blue-tailed is one of the commonest species nationally and is widespread in the County. It frequents both still and slow moving waters, flying low over the surface or amongst marginal vegetation. Although it is tolerant of a wide range of water conditions, it prefers neutral or slightly alkaline water; however it can also be found on the heathlands, on brackish pools and even in slightly polluted waters.

The Scarce Blue-tailed Damselfly is a national rarity and is restricted to the south-western counties of England and Wales, where it frequents boggy pools on the heathlands; and to a few gravel pits and other mineral workings in the Midlands. Its numbers vary considerably from year to year and, when abundant, it may be encountered in unexpected habitats, such as watercress beds or casual pools.

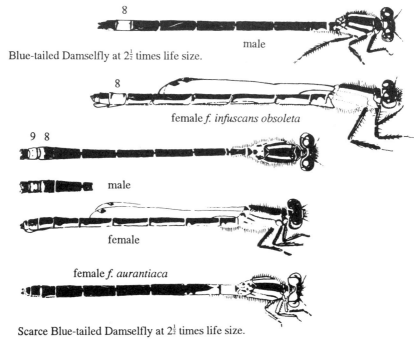

8

male

Blue-tailed Damselfly at $2\frac{1}{2}$ times life size.

8

female *f. infuscans obsoleta*

9 8

male

female

female *f. aurantiaca*

Scarce Blue-tailed Damselfly at $2\frac{1}{2}$ times life size.

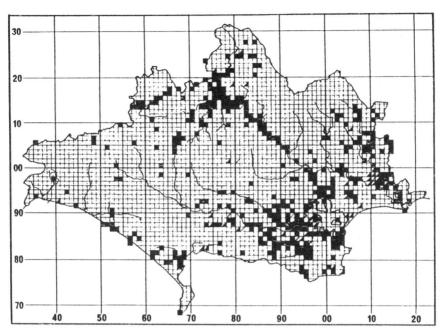

Map 11. Distribution map of Blue-tailed Damselfly, *Ischnura elegans.*

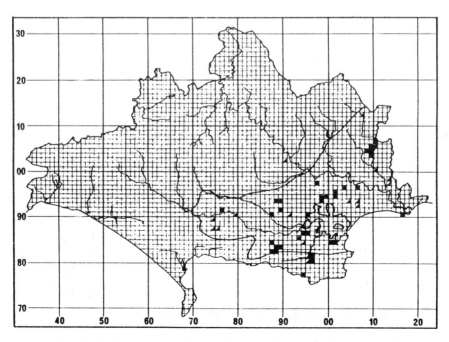

Map 12. Distribution map of Scarce Blue-tailed Damselfly, *Ischnura pumilio.*

SOUTHERN DAMSELFLY
Coenagrion mercuriale

RED-EYED DAMSELFLY
Erythromma najas
Map 13

The Southern Damselfly is the smallest and scarcest blue damselfly that occurs in Dorset. It is like the Azure Damselfly in general pattern and colouration. The most important distinguishing feature is the mark on segment 2 of the male which has a 'mercury' sign; the rest of the abdomen is blue with black markings. The mark on this segment of the female is a 'thistle-head' which is normally on a greenish background: the remainder of the abdomen is black with pale bands encircling the joints of the segments.

The Southern Damselfly is one of the rarest damselflies in Britain. Its strongholds are the New Forest, where it is locally abundant, the Presceli Mountains and the Gower Peninsula. Elsewhere, it occurs in a few scattered localities including the Isle of Purbeck. Here it is seldom found far from small boggy patches and overgrown waterways, where it breeds. A stable supply of calcareous water in well vegetated channels seems to be an essential requirement for breeding.

The Red-eyed Damselfly is not uncommon in the Midlands and south-east England. In Dorset there are recent records from only ten sites, all of which are flooded pits or artificial ponds. At first glance, it looks not unlike a larger and more robust Blue-tailed Damselfly, but the outstanding red eyes of the male are unmistakable. The thorax and abdomen are black, with the exception of segments 1, 9, and 10 which are blue. Only segment 8 of the Blue-tailed Damselfly is blue. The female is similar, but has red-brown eyes and short brown thoracic stripes: her abdomen is mainly black except for some yellow on segment 1.

The Red-eyed Damselfly is a powerful flier, which likes large ponds, where it usually keeps some way out from the shore. Ponds with pondweed *Potamogeton* spp., water-lilies and other floating vegetation, on which they rest, are favoured by the males who periodically make sweeps low over the water surface. The females keep more to the marginal vegetation.

In view of its scarcity there is no distribution map for the Southern Damselfly.

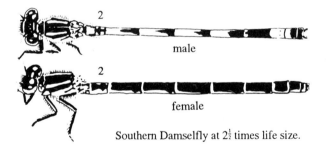

male

female

Southern Damselfly at $2\frac{1}{2}$ times life size.

male

female

Red-eyed Damselfly at $2\frac{1}{2}$ times life size.

32

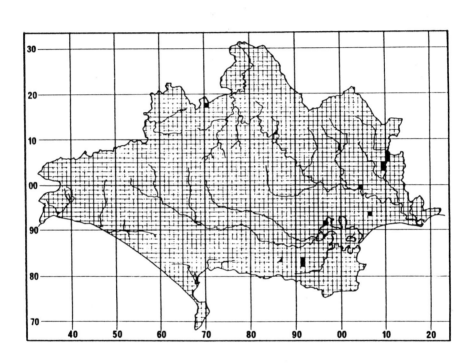

Map 13. Distribution map of Red-eyed Damselfly, *Erythromma najas*.

LARGE RED DAMSELFLY
Pyrrhosoma nymphula
Map 14

SMALL RED DAMSELFLY
Ceriagrion tenellum
Map 15

The Large Red Damselfly is a sturdy insect, which is common throughout much of the British Isles. It often occurs in large numbers by either still or running waters, which may be anything from slightly alkaline to slightly acidic. It is frequently the earliest species to emerge in the spring and is one of the first to colonise new garden or farm ponds.

The adult males are mainly bright red with black legs; the thorax is black with red stripes and abdominal segments 7 to 9 largely dark bronze. The females are similar to the males, but are stouter and have yellow bands encircling each joint of the abdomen, a dark line running along the top of segments 2 to 6, and dark markings by the segments joints. The females vary considerably and some forms have pale yellow thoracic stripes and completely black abdomens - *melanotum* - while others have a much thinner dorsal stripe and fewer dark markings on the abdomen - *fulvipes*.

By contrast, the Small Red Damselfly, which is a national rarity, is a smaller, slighter insect. It is confined to acid *Sphagnum* bogs, seepages and the marshy margins of heathland pools. Its strongholds, where it is often locally numerous, are the heathlands of Dorset, Hampshire, Sussex and Surrey, with further populations on the moors of south-west England and west Wales.

It can be distinguished from the Large Red Damselfly by its small size, red - not black - legs, a bronze top to most of the thorax and, in the males, an all red abdomen. The normal female is mostly bronze on the abdomen, except for segments 1 to 3 which are red. She can likewise be distinguished by size, leg colour and bronze thorax with only faint stripes. As in the Large Red Damselfly there are variations - one form *erythrogastrum* resembles the male with an all red abdomen.

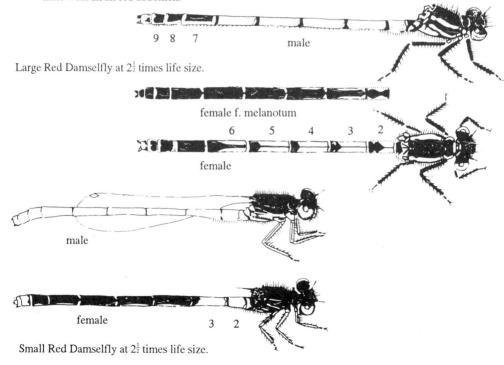

9 8 7   male

Large Red Damselfly at 2½ times life size.

female f. melanotum

6   5   4   3   2

female

male

female   3   2

Small Red Damselfly at 2½ times life size.

34

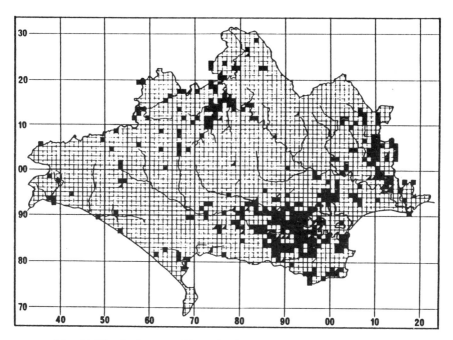

Map 14. Distribution map of Large Red Damselfly, *Pyrrhosoma nymphula.*

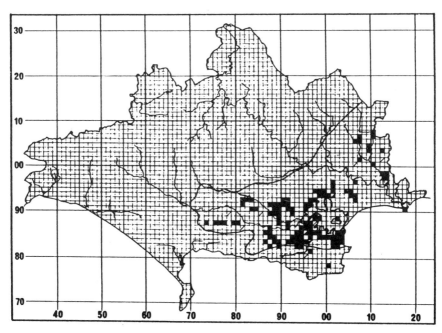

Map 15. Distribution map of Small Red Damselfly, *Ceriagrion tenellum.*

COMMON HAWKER
Aeshna juncea
Map 16

SOUTHERN HAWKER
Aeshna cyanea
Map 17 (p. 42)

The hawkers are powerful fliers. These are two large somewhat similar species with clear wings and long deep-brown bodies marked with green, blue and yellow. The chief differences may be summarised:

	Common Hawker	Southern Hawker
Thoracic stripes	Male: narrow, orange Female: none	Broad apple-green
Costa	Bright yellow	Brown
Abdomen	Spots throughout	Segments: 1-7 green spots
	Male: blue	Male: 8 blue spots 9, 10 blue bar
	Female: green	Female: 8, 9, 10 green bar

The Common Hawker is mainly an upland species with a preference for acidic waters. It is to be found in most places where these occur and is widely distributed in Scotland, northern England, Wales and the southern heathlands of England. Besides being regularly found in the Poole Basin, it is sparsely distributed elsewhere in Dorset.

The Southern Hawker is widespread south of a line from the Humber to the Mersey; northwards it is scarce and has rarely been reported from Scotland. In Dorset it is much commoner than the so-called Common Hawker. It may be found not only besides ponds but almost anywhere, especially where there are country lanes, sheltered rides and scrubby hedgerows. It is the most inquisitive of the dragon-flies and one sometimes finds oneself being inspected closely by a hovering insect before it darts off in search of food.

The Common Hawker often flies over ponds and streams on a regular beat, but it can also be found in similar places to the Southern Hawker. With experience the males can be distinguished in flight; the Common Hawker appearing generally brown and blue while the Southern appears to be much greener. Usually it is best to wait until the insect settles - which it does fairly frequently, hanging vertically from a branch or stalk - for certain identification.

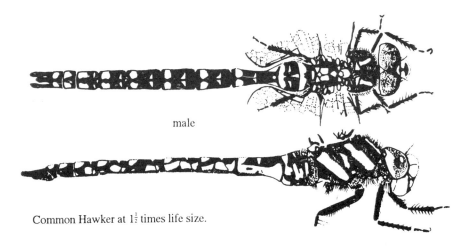

male

Common Hawker at 1½ times life size.

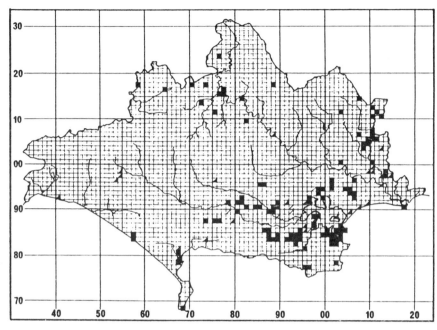

Map 16. Distribution map of Common Hawker, *Aeshna juncea*.

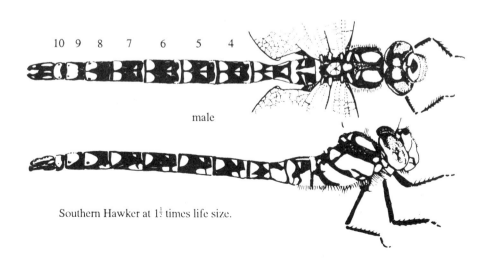

male

Southern Hawker at 1½ times life size.

MIGRANT HAWKER	BROWN HAWKER
Aeshna mixta	*Aeshna grandis*
Map 18	Map 19

The Migrant Hawker is a widespread Continental species. It is the smallest of the hawkers that occur in Dorset and, although once considered to be only a migrant to Britain, is now a well established breeder in many parts of the country especially in the south-east. It appears to be extending its range in Britain. In Dorset there were few reported away from the coasts until 1984 when some were present in the Blackmore Vale, followed by increased numbers in the following years: in autumn 1990 it was common along the River Stour from Blandford to above Sturminster Newton.

The Migrant Hawker is less aggressive than most dragon-flies and several may be found together in favoured localities, such as sheltered lanes or stretches of water with or without reeds. They frequently hover, especially over water, and often zoom up into the air in pursuit of their prey; characteristics which, combined with their small size, distinguish them in flight from the somewhat similar Common Hawker. The patterns and colours of their abdomens are indeed similar but, when settled, the Migrant Hawker can be separated from the Common Hawker by the generally paler appearance of its eyes and thorax, the thoracic stripes which are pale or lacking, a brown (not yellow) costa and a yellow triangle on segment 2. In the male, segment 3 has a characteristic cream mark which turns blue with age. Though reputed to be easily disturbed and very wary, it is not always so, and is sometimes confiding, although not to the same extent as the Southern Hawker.

The Brown Hawker is unmistakable, even from a distance, with its brown body - dark in males and light in females - and amber-brown wings, which are particularly conspicuous in sunlight. It is slightly larger than the Common and Southern Hawkers, and has somewhat similar habits. It is less often seen away from water and generally prefers open country to constricted lanes and rides.

Its distribution in England is mainly to the south of the Humber-Mersey line. Dorset lies near its south-western limit, which seems to be from Poole Harbour to Bridgwater Bay with only isolated records further west. The Blackmore Vale would appear to be the stronghold of the Brown Hawker in the County, but this may be because it has been overlooked elsewhere.

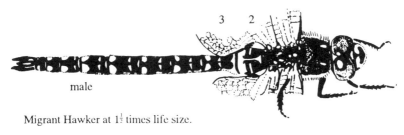

male

Migrant Hawker at $1\frac{1}{3}$ times life size.

male

Brown Hawker at $1\frac{1}{3}$ times life size.

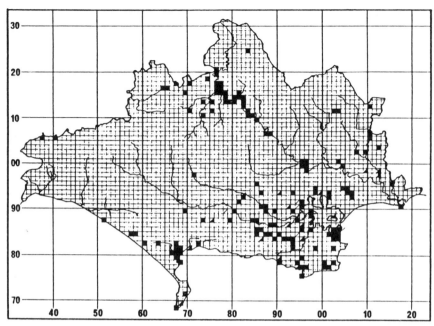

Map 18. Distribution map of Migrant Hawker, *Aeshna mixta.*

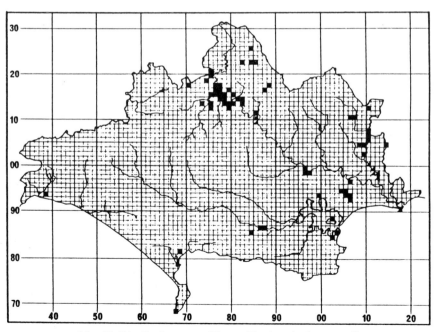

Map 19. Distribution map of Brown Hawker, *Aeshna grandis.*

EMPEROR DRAGON-FLY
Anax imperator
Map 20

GOLDEN-RINGED DRAGON-FLY
Cordulegaster boltoni
Map 21 (p. 42)

The handsome Emperor Dragon-fly is well named: it is a powerful flier, brightly marked and overall the largest British dragonfly. It dominates its chosen lake or pond chasing away other dragon-flies and damselflies when it is not preying on them or other insects. It is rarely seen far from still water, preferring well vegetated sites over which it patrols tirelessly; its abdomen curved slightly downwards in characteristic fashion, a feature which helps to distinguish it in flight from other large dragon-flies. Both sexes have an unstriped apple-green thorax and thick markings (black on the male and deep brown on the female) down the centre of their dark almost uniformly coloured abdomens. The latter are rich blue in males and some old females, and green with a brownish tip in normal females.

Nationally the Emperor Dragon-fly becomes increasingly common southwards of a line from Cardigan Bay to the Wash. It is widely distributed in Dorset and occurs wherever there are suitable ponds, gravel pits or slow-running waters. It is never numerous as only large stretches of water can accommodate more than one male.

Although the Emperor Dragon-fly is overall the largest, the female Golden-ringed can claim to be the longest bodied, due to its long ovipositor. The sexes are alike: overall black with yellow thoracic stripes and yellow rings around the abdomen, which, especially in the males, has a noticeable waist. Its size and yellow and black markings make it easy to recognise.

The Golden-ringed Dragon-fly is fond of flying low along a fast flowing stream on a settled beat, which may extend over adjacent heaths and young plantations. With its preference for acidic waters, its strongholds in Dorset are the heathlands of the Poole Basin, but it may be found on streams and ponds elsewhere in the County. It is widely distributed in Scotland, Wales, north-west and southern England, but absent from the Midlands and East Anglia.

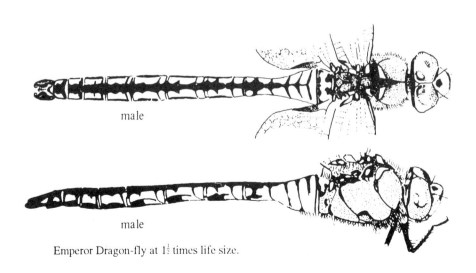

male

male

Emperor Dragon-fly at 1½ times life size.

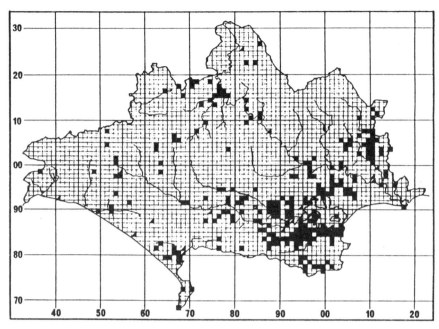

Map 20. Distribution map of Emperor Dragon-fly, *Anax imperator*.

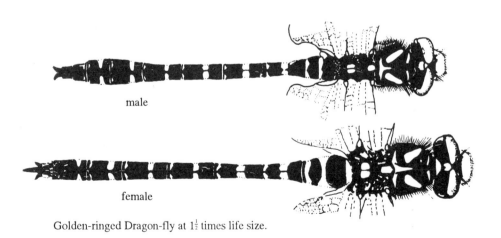

male

female

Golden-ringed Dragon-fly at $1\frac{1}{2}$ times life size.

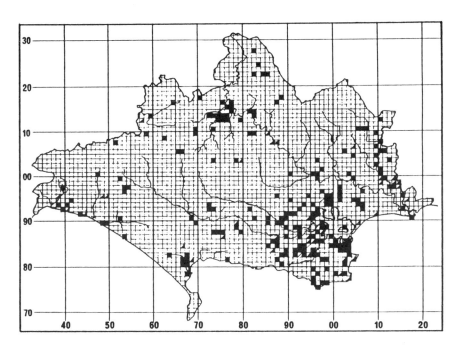

Map 17. Distribution map of Southern Hawker, *Aeshna cyanea.*

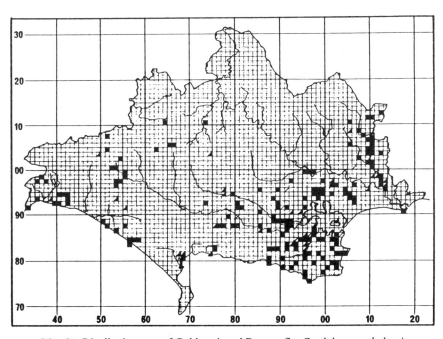

Map 21. Distribution map of Golden-ringed Dragon-fly, *Cordulegaster boltoni.*

42

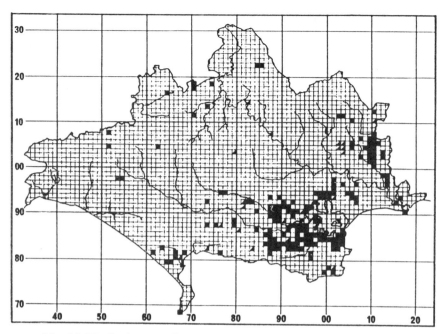

Map 24. Distribution map of Four-spotted Chaser, *Libellula quadrimaculata.*

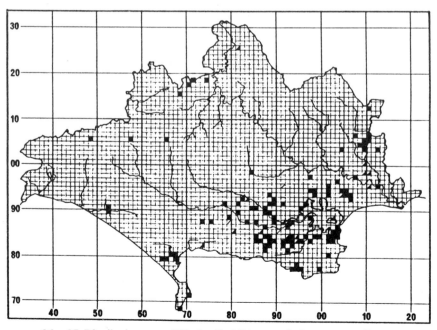

Map 27. Distribution map of Black-tailed Skimmer, *Orthetrum cancellatum.*

43

DOWNY EMERALD
Cordulia aenea
Map 22

ORANGE-SPOTTED EMERALD
Oxygastra curtisi

The beautiful bronze-green Downy Emerald is not uncommon in the south of England: the main populations are in Sussex, Kent, Surrey, Hampshire and the Poole Basin in Dorset. It has also been recorded in isolated pockets elsewhere, notably in the west of England, Gloucestershire, and in west Scotland. The sexes are similar, with bright green eyes and a thorax covered with downy hair. The males are usually found patrolling tree-sheltered ponds on heathland, where they fly fast and low over the water. In flight they appear to be shiny black except for their transparent wings. Females may be more often seen away from water, hawking in sheltered glades.

The Orange-spotted Emerald was first discovered in Britain, by the famous Dorset entomologist J.C. Dale of Glanville's Wootton, on Parley Heath (then in Hampshire) on 29th of June 1820, and shortly afterwards at Hurn in Dorset. He named it after his great friend the distinguished entomologist John Curtis. It was initially thought to be endemic to Britain but it has since been found to be widespread on the Continent; Britain being at the northern edge of its range. Besides Dorset and Hampshire, it has been recorded from Devon.

It was well known from the Moors River, but has now disappeared from there and everywhere else in Britain. Dr N.W. Moore last found it on the Moors River in 1957 (Moore 1991), and Col F.C. Fraser and other entomologists are reported to have kept it under observation until 1963, when it was no longer to be found (Brown 1988). Despite much searching, it has not subsequently been seen.

The Orange-spotted Emerald resembles the Downy Emerald in size and in the general metallic green colour of its abdomen. It is distinguished by having conspicuous yellow dorsal markings on the abdomen, which is very narrow at the base and broadens at the tip.

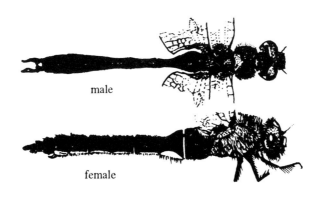

male

female

Downy Emerald at 1½ times life size.

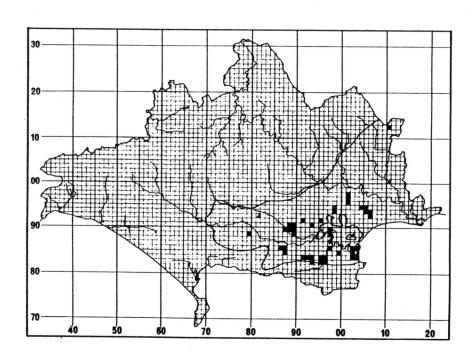

Map 22. Distribution map of Downy Emerald, *Cordulia aenea.*

HAIRY DRAGON-FLY
Brachytron pratense
p. 8 Map 23

The Hairy Dragon-fly is the smallest of the hawkers. It has the hairiest thorax of any British dragonfly, only the male having conspicuous green (yellow when immature) thoracic stripes. The abdomen of both sexes is dark brown to black with twin pear-shaped spots on segments 2 - 10, sky-blue in the male and yellow in the female; a feature which makes her easily recognisable. The male can be confused with the Common Hawker but, besides small colour differences, the latter is about 25% larger. Furthermore, their flight periods scarcely overlap: the Hairy Dragon-fly flies from the middle of May until the end of June and the Common Hawker from late June until September.

Although the Hairy Dragon-fly is generally scarce, it is fairly common at some places in southern England. It is usually associated with canals and slow-running rivers in coastal plains and flood levels, such as those in Kent, Sussex and in Somerset. In Dorset it is most often found on the heathlands, on ponds and along ditches and streams.

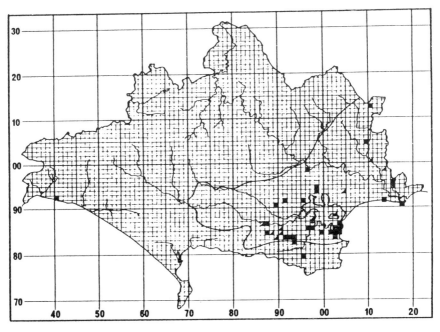

Map 23. Distribution map of Hairy Dragon-fly, *Brachytron pratense*.

FOUR-SPOTTED CHASER
Libellula quadrimaculata
Map 24 (p. 43)

The three chasers that occur in Britain, the Four-spotted, Broad-bodied and Scarce, all have broad squat abdomens and conspicuous dark brown patches at the bases of their hind wings.

Of the three species, only the Four-spotted has a dark brown mark at the nodus in addition to a blackish pterostigma on each wing. Altogether it has eight spots on its wings. The sexes are alike, with their brown abdomens edged with yellow when seen from above, and the final four segments are black. Unlike the other two chasers, it never acquires any pruinescence - a powder-blue exudation which covers the abdomen as the insect ages. The specimen illustrated is an uncommon form, *praenubila*, which has more extensive wingbase patches and dark smokey marks near the wing tips.

The Four-spotted Chaser prefers acidic, still waters and is chiefly found around boggy heathland pools where, on the larger waters especially in the early part of the season, there may be several males each defending his own sector.

Nationally the Four-spotted Chaser is widespread except in the north-east of England. In Dorset, it occurs mainly in the Poole Basin but there are scattered records from elsewhere.

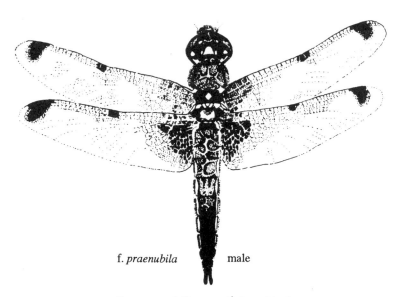

f. *praenubila*   male

Four-spotted Chaser at 1½ times life size.

BROAD-BODIED CHASER
Libellula depressa
Map 25

SCARCE CHASER
Libellula fulva
Map 26

The Broad-bodied Chaser, like the other chasers, has brown markings at the bases of its hind wings, but it is distinguished from them by its wide abdomen. Young males and females are alike in having brown abdomens with yellow spots on their sides. They are very similar to the Four-spotted Chaser but, besides being much broader, lack the black tip to the abdomen and have only a single black spot (the pterostigma) on each wing. As the males age, the brown centre of the abdomen becomes covered with a blue pruinescence and the yellow spots darken. A few old females similarly change colour. Both sexes have, on the brown thorax, bluish-yellow stripes which are more generally pronounced in the male than in the female.

The Broad-bodied Chaser, which is common in Dorset and elsewhere in southern England, is a still water species and is usually found on alkaline ponds and ditches, though it tolerates slightly acidic waters. The males are very territorial and often have a favourite perch on a branch or reed to which they return between sorties to capture prey or chase away rivals.

The Scarce Chaser has its strongholds on parts of the Broads, the River Ouse and in the Poole Basin. It is to be found chiefly on slow running rivers, and in Dorset it is not uncommon on some stretches of the Frome, Stour and Moors rivers. Although generally similar, it is more slender than the Broad-bodied Chaser and lacks its thoracic stripes. The young males and females also lack the yellow spots on the sides of their orange-brown abdomens, and have a conspicuous black mark down the centre of segments 3 to 10. The female has a brown patch on each wing tip. In old males, as with the Broad-bodied, the abdomen gets covered with a blue pruinescence, except for a black triangular mark from segments 7 to 10. They frequently have irregular dark marks on segments 5 and 6 where the pruinescence has been abraded by the clasping of the female during mating. Males of the Scarce Chaser showing pruinescence can be confused with Black-tailed Skimmer males, but the latter lack the dark wing bases of the chasers.

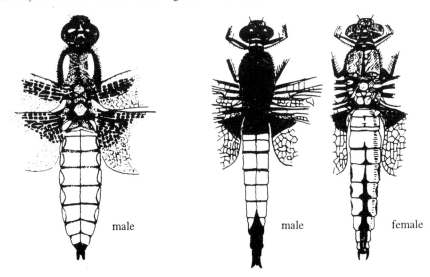

male   male   female

Broad-bodied Chaser at 1½ times life size.   Scarce Chaser at 1½ times life size.

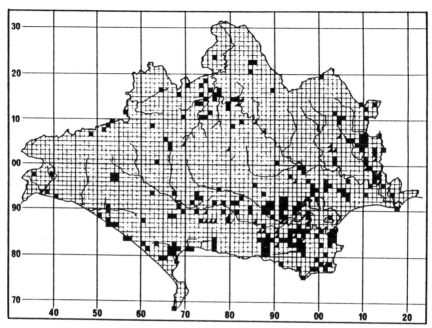

Map 25. Distribution map of Broad-bodied Chaser, *Libellula depressa.*

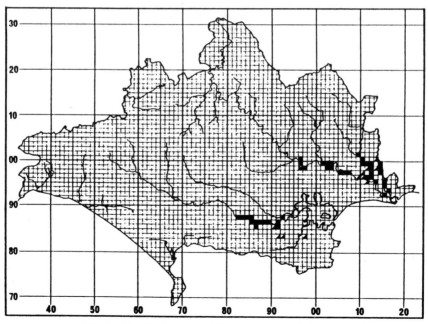

Map 26. Distribution map of Scarce Chaser, *Libellula fulva.*

BLACK-TAILED SKIMMER
Orthetrum cancellatum
Map 27 (p. 43)

KEELED SKIMMER
Orthetrum coerulescens
Map 28

These two skimmers are medium sized dragon-flies. They are smaller than hawkers but larger than darters. At first sight they can be confused with chasers but they lack the squat abdomens and brown wing bases of the latter.

The Black-tailed Skimmer is the larger of the two. It is a stronger flier, has no dorsal stripes and the male always has segments 8 to 10 black. The rest of the abdomen in the male, and the entire abdomen in the female, is yellow at first with two black longitudinal scalloped markings. With age these segments in the male become covered with a blue pruinescence while the abdomen of the female turns tawny-brown. The Black-tailed Skimmer is usually found on large shallow ponds and gravel pits, where the males spend long periods settled motionless on old reeds or bare patches by the edge of the water. From these perches they make sorties, skimming over the surface of the pond. It is often one of the first dragon-flies to colonise new ponds.

The Keeled Skimmer is much more an inhabitant of moorlands where it breeds in *Sphagnum* bogs. On some of these it is very common and can be seen flying low over the heather and bogs. When young both sexes have yellow-brown abdomens and well-defined pale thoracic stripes. On maturity, the entire abdomen of the male becomes covered with pruinescence. The female has a fine black dorsal line down the length of her abdomen, and slightly clouded wings, the bases of which are suffused with amber. The pterostigma of both sexes is pale orange, in contrast to the black of the Black-tailed Skimmer.

Neither species can be regarded as common in Britain as a whole, though each is abundant in some areas. The Black-tailed Skimmer is mainly restricted to the south of the Severn-Wash line, where it is frequent in counties with water-filled gravel pits; but with few records from Devon and Cornwall. These latter two counties, together with Dorset, Hampshire and Surrey, hold most of the colonies of the Keeled Skimmer; which also occurs in Wales and isolated localities as far north as the Isle of Skye.

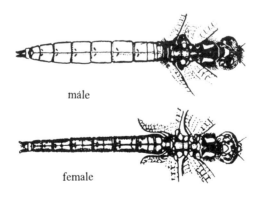

male

female

Keeled Skimmer at 1½ times life size.

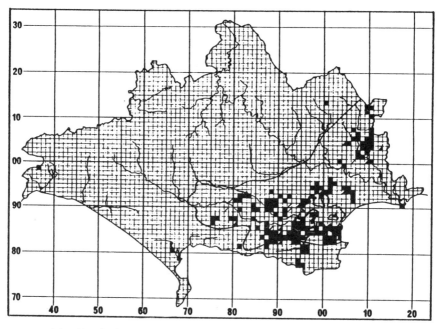

Map 28. Distribution map of Keeled Skimmer, *Orthetrum coerulescens.*

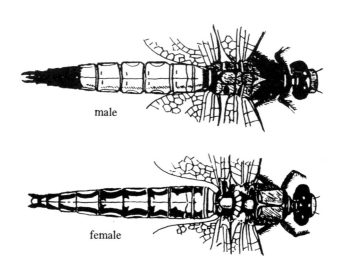

male

female

Black-tailed Skimmer at 1½ times life size.

51

BLACK DARTER
Sympetrum danae
Map 29

The darters, which are the smallest British dragon-flies, are represented in Dorset by three breeding species and two vagrants. The males of the two largest breeding species, the Common Darter and the Ruddy Darter, are mainly red whilst the third is the aptly named Black Darter. The Black Darter rarely strays far from the acidic bogs and heaths. Nationally it is widespread where these occur: in Dorset it is confined to the Poole Basin, where on the heaths in the autumn it is often the commonest dragon-fly. It has a restless darting flight, usually of short duration, and often returns to the same spot, which may be bare ground, a sprig of heather or some other vegetation.

The mature Black Darter has a completely black body, with segments 3 to 5 constricted, black legs and - like the female - clear, black-veined wings with a black pterostigma. The females and young males are alike: they are yellow-brown with a large conspicuous black triangle on the top of the thorax. The females resemble those of the Common and Ruddy Darters: in the hand or in the net, the side of the thorax should be examined. As can be seen below, on the Black Darter there is a heavy black band with three yellow spots: on the Common Darter and Ruddy Darter there are only thin black lines on a yellow background (p. 54).

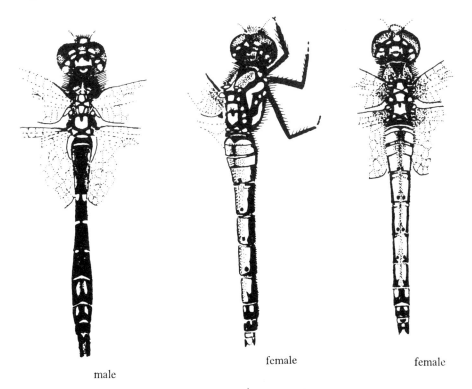

male

female

female

Black Darter at 2½ times life size.

52

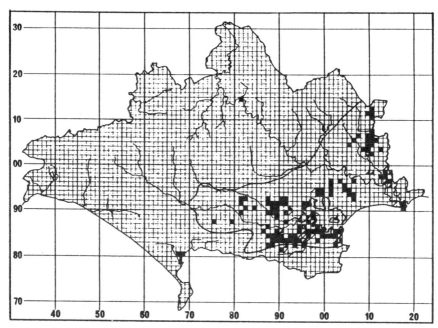

Map 29. Distribution map of Black Darter, *Sympetrum danae.*

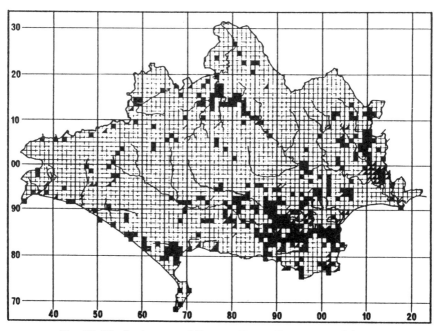

Map 30. Distribution map of Common Darter, *Sympetrum striolatum.*

COMMON DARTER
Sympetrum striolatum
Map 30 (p. 53)

RUDDY DARTER
Sympetrum sanguineum
Map 31

The Common Darter and the Ruddy Darter are generally similar, with their mainly clear wings, absence of thoracic stripes, and red (male) or yellowish-brown (female) abdomens; but the males, in particular, are not too difficult to tell apart. Amongst other differences, the Ruddy Darter is smaller and a quicker flyer with a characteristic jerky flight.

The abdomen of the Common Darter is almost parallel-sided and is dull red, except for a pair of small black dots on segments 3 to 8, and a small black mark on each of segments 8 and 9. The Ruddy Darter's abdomen, by contrast, is blood-red, with a marked waist due to constricted segments 3 to 5, and prominent oblong black marks on segments 8 and 9. Other differences are the richer brown colour of the thorax of the Ruddy Darter and the leg colour - brown striped with yellow in the Common, and black in the Ruddy. The leg colour is the same in both sexes and is a useful distinguishing point for the females. The female Keeled Skimmer is somewhat similar, but differs in having prominent pale thoracic stripes, a thin black line down the top of the abdomen and slightly clouded wings.

The Common Darter is widespread and common throughout Dorset and indeed most of England and Wales. It may be found almost anywhere and is equally at home on the heathlands, along rivers, on pools and lakes, on the chalklands and even on brackish ponds. Both the range and the habitat of the Ruddy Darter is more restricted; it prefers well-vegetated ponds, slow-running rivers and ditches, particularly those with Reed Mace *Typha latifolia*. Nationally, its main stronghold is to the south-east of a line from the Wash to the Severn; though there are a fair number of records from Dorset, it has seldom been reported from Devon or Cornwall. However, both the Ruddy and Common Darters may turn up anywhere, as the local breeding populations are periodically reinforced by immigrants from the Continent.

Both species like to bask on light patches of gravel, flattened vegetation, bits of wood and similar reflective surfaces, from which they make frequent short flights before returning to their perch.

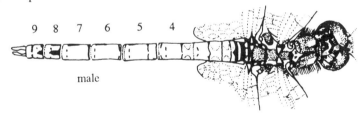

9 8 7 6 5 4

male

Common Darter at 2½ times life size.

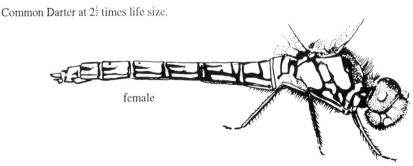

female

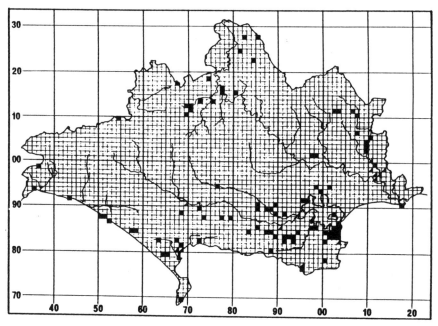

Map 31. Distribution map of Ruddy Darter, *Sympetrum sanguineum*.

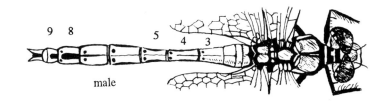

Ruddy Darter at $2\frac{1}{2}$ times life size.

VAGRANTS

YELLOW-WINGED DARTER *Sympetrum flaveolum*

An infrequent visitor from the Continent. Most records are from the south-east of England. This species was found in Dorset in 1934 and 1944. Dr. N.W. Moore reported one from Stoborough Heath on 19th July 1946. The only recent record is from Warmwell Heath on 30th September 1973. The Yellow-winged Darter is about the same size as the Common Darter, from which it is distinguished by the saffron patches at the bases of its wings. On the hind wing this patch may cover up to one third of the wing area.

RED-VEINED DARTER *Sympetrum fonscolombei*

The Red-veined Darter is a rare vagrant from Europe. It is the most beautiful of the darters with a crimson costa, numerous red veins and a bluish tinge to its wings. There are a few records for the County. Col. F.C. Fraser saw quite a number near Bournemouth in 1941, and prior to this Dr F.H. Haines used to take specimens on West Knighton Heath and on the Decoy Pond at Morden. After an immigration in 1911 it bred in the County until 1915. There are no recent reports, Dorset apparently missing out on the minor irruption in 1984 when there were several records for Devon and Cornwall.

VAGRANT EMPEROR DRAGON-FLY *Hemianax ephippiger*

The Vagrant Emperor Dragon-fly is a great wanderer from the Middle East and the more arid parts of Africa, where it is very common and breeds even in desert oases and temporary pools. It is the only species to have been recorded from Iceland, and has occurred about a dozen times in Britain, including once at Portland in August 1983. It is large and generally light sandy-brown in colour with a conspicuous saddle on segment 2, just behind the wings; which is brilliant blue in the male and somewhat duller in the female.

CLUB-TAILED DRAGON-FLY *Gomphus vulgatissimus*

There are a few old reports of this striking medium-sized black dragon-fly with extensive greenish yellow markings, but no evidence that it has ever been anything but a stray from neighbouring counties. Nationally it is rare, and confined to a few major river valleys, such as the Thames and Severn. Its distinctive colouration, widely spaced eyes and early flight period (mid May to end of June) make it unmistakable.

CHAPTER 3. COLLECTING DRAGONFLIES IN THE UNITED KINGDOM
British Dragonfly Society Code of Practice 1988

Assumptions and background information

Dragonflies should not be killed unnecessarily. Identification can often be achieved by observation, photography and by collecting exuviae, especially in the countries like the United Kingdom where much is known about the Odonata fauna already. It is also possible to capture dragonflies, examine them and then release them undamaged. They should be released where they were caught and as soon as possible afterwards.

Dragonflies should only be killed when a useful purpose is served thereby. For example, the conservation value of faunistic surveys, local lists etc. depends upon the reliability of accurate taxonomic identification. Where any doubt exists an identifiable photograph should be taken or an identifiable drawing made, but when this is not possible a voucher specimen should be collected.

The main concern is to prevent significant damage to populations, especially those of rare and vulnerable species.

All the evidence suggests that collecting is almost always a negligible cause of damage to dragonfly populations, whereas serious and lasting damage can be caused by destruction or pollution of habitats. Nevertheless it is highly desirable to reduce risks as far as possible, and to promote a conservation ethic. If children are not allowed to collect at all, they are less likely to become interested in dragonflies and, hence, they will not become concerned about their conservation. A balance has to be struck between preventing risk and engendering interest and study.

The occasions when dragonflies can legitimately be collected

a) Rare and vulnerable species and isolated populations of common species

    i)   Collecting voucher specimens when exuviae are not available.

    ii) Collecting specimens as a necessary part of a study whose objective is to conserve the population/species concerned.

b) Common species

    i)   Collecting specimens for reference in personal and institutional collections.

    ii) Collecting specimens for serious scientific research; eg anatomical, physiological, ecological or ethological studies.

    iv) Collecting specimens for teaching purposes.

    v)   Collecting specimens for display for educational and/or conservation purposes.

Points to be observed when collecting

The following have been adapted from the Code for Insect Collecting issued by the Joint Committee for the Conservation of British Insects. Bulletin of the Amateur Entomologists' Society, 31:99-101. (1972).

1. No more specimens than are strictly necessary for any purpose should be killed.

2. Readily identified species should not be killed if the object is to 'look them over' for aberrations or for other purposes: if possible insects should be examined while alive and then released where they were captured.

3. The same species should not be taken in numbers year after year from the same locality.

4. Specimens for exchange or disposal to other collectors should be taken sparingly or not at all.

5. Permission should always be sought from the landowner or occupier when collecting (or studying) on private land.

6. Conditions laid down by the grantor of permission to collect should always be complied with.

7. When collections are made on nature reserves or sites known to conservationists, a list of species collected (or observed) should be supplied to those responsible for managing the site.

8. The environment should be damaged as little as possible. Remember the needs of other organisms and the interests of other naturalists: be careful of vegetation, nesting birds and particularly rare species.

9. Waterweed and moss which has been worked for larvae should not be left on the bank but should be replaced in the water.

10.   Discretion should be exercised when passing on, or making public, the location of rare and vulnerable species.

Collecting dragonflies and the Law

The Norfolk Hawker *Anaciaeschna isosceles* (*Müller, 1767*) is currently the only species totally protected under the Wildlife and Countryside Act 1981.

CHAPTER 4 THE FOSSIL DRAGONFLIES OF DORSET

by

Ed. Jarzembowski

To anyone interested in the history of dragonflies, Dorset is an essential source, having yielded at least fourteen fossil species from rocks belonging to three major geological periods and spanning some 155 million years. The geological strata get progressively younger from west to east across the area and so our survey commences near Lyme Regis (Table 3).

Middle Eocene	Bournemouth Freshwater Beds	48
Lower Cretaceous	Durlston Formation	
		144
Upper Jurassic	Lulworth Formation	
Lower Jurassic	Lower Lias	203

Notes:
1. The numbers indicate approximate 'absolute' ages in millions of years Before Present based on Harland et al: (1982).
2. The Bournemouth Freshwater Beds are the Bagshot Sands of earlier authors; some modern workers refer to these strata as the Bournemouth or Bracklesham Formation (see Daley and Crewdson, 1987).
3. The Lulworth and Durlston Formations are equivalent to the Lower, Middle and Upper Purbeck Beds of earlier authors (Townson, 1975); the Durlston Formation is assigned to the Wealden Series (or Beds; Allen, 1976).

Table 3: Dorset insect-bearing rocks

Some 200 million years ago, the eroding cliffs of Charmouth were lime mud accumulating on an early Jurassic sea floor and these ancient liassic deposits are renowned for their fossil marine reptiles and ammonites. Occasionally, terrestrial organisms such as winged insects found their way out to sea. Two clayey limestones in the zone of the ammonite *Asteroceras obtusum* have yielded the remains of seven extinct species of Odonata (Table 4), all found by the late Mr J.F. Jackson and first described by Professor Zeuner (1962). Prior to retiring to Charmouth, Jackson was the curator of the Sandown Museum, Isle of Wight and would have been familiar with fossil insects on account of the 'Insect Limestone' occurring on the island. History had come nearly a full circle because, a century earlier, a retired sailor discovered the 'Insect Limestone' due to its similarity to insect-bearing rocks in Purbeck!

The tripartite classification of living Odonata has been applied to fossils and the Charmouth dragonflies, with their supposed damselfly-like features, were referred by Zeuner to the Anisozygoptera, today represented only by two Asian species in the genus *Epiophlebia* (Asahina, 1954). Subsequently, Pritykina (1980) considered as most important the damselfly (Zygoptera)-like features of fossil 'Anisozygoptera' whereas Carle (1982) stressed their relationship with true dragon-flies (Anisoptera). However, fossil 'Anisozygoptera' usually have a distinct venation and show that Odonata had already become quite specialised by Jurassic times.

'Suborder Anisozygoptera' (of authors)

    Family Tarsophlebiidae

        1)   *Tarsophlebia?* sp. Jarzembowski 1987.

           Durlston Formation, Durlston Bay.

    Family Liassophlebiidae

        2)   *Liassophlebia pseudomagnifica* Whalley 1985.

           Lower Lias, Charmouth.

        3)   *Liassophlebia jacksoni* Zeuner 1962.

           Lower Lias, Charmouth.

        4)   *Liassophlebia gigantea* Zeuner 1962.

           Lower Lias, Charmouth.

        5)   *Liassophlebia anglicanopsis* (Zeuner 1962) Whalley 1985

           Lower Lias Charmouth.

        6)   *Hypsothemis fraseri* Whalley 1985.

           Lower Lias, Charmouth.

    Family Archithemistidae

        7)   *Dorsettia laeta* Whalley 1985.

           Lower Lias, Charmouth.

    Family Heterophlebiidae

        8)   *Heterophlebia* sp. Whalley 1985

           Lower Lias, Charmouth.

Suborder Anisoptera

    Family Aeschnidiidae

        9)   *Aeschnidium bubas* Westwood 1854

           Lulworth Formation, Durlston Bay.

    'Family Gomphidae' (of authors)

        10) *Cymatophlebiopsis pseudobubas* Handlirsch 1939.

           Lulworth Formation, Durlston Bay.

        11) *Mesogomphus* sp. new record

           Lulworth Formation, 'Fossil Forest' (G. Miller collection).

    'Family Petaluridae' (of authors)

        12) *Cymatophlebia?* agrias (Westwood 1854) Handlirsch 1906.

           Lulworth Formation, Durlston Bay.

    Family Aeshnidae

        13) *Triaeschna gossi* Campion 1916.

           Bournemouth Freshwater Beds, Bournemouth.

    Anisoptera: family uncertain

        14) *Agrionidium aetna* Westwood 1854.

           Lulworth Formation, Durlston Bay.

Table 4 - Checklist of Dorset fossil Odonata.

About 146 million years ago, the Jurassic sea retreated from southern England to be replaced by a variety of non-marine and marine marginal environments which continued into early Cretaceous times. The newly emerged lowland was colonised by various terrestrial and freshwater animals including dinosaurs and dragonflies. In Dorset, insect fossils occur in several limestone beds in the 'Isle' of Purbeck, the typical outcrop area of the Purbeck Beds of earlier writers (Table 3). As in the Lias, Odonata are represented by adult remains but insects are generally more fragmented and concentrated as if under the influence of the streams and rivers which they undoubtedly bordered or frequented. The climate was somewhat arid at first, becoming more humid later (Sladen & Batten, 1984) and it is interesting to note that specimens from the Lulworth Formation are usually oxidised impressions in whitish limestone, whereas those from the Durlston Formation are in blue-grey limestone with organic remains. Dorset dragonflies had changed during the Jurassic and the late Jurassic - early Cretaceous fauna is dominated by true dragon-flies (Anisoptera) although no living families are yet recognised for sure (Table 4). Gomphid-like and petalurid-like forms are found as well as an extinct family (Aeschnidiidae) with a characteristic libellulid-like triangle and dense cross venation.

The youngest recorded fossil dragonfly in this area is *Triaeschna gossi* from the Middle Eocene of Bournemouth (previously in Hampshire). This extinct aeshnid or 'hawker' dragon-fly is known from a solitary wing found in pipeclay deposits during the last century. The clay is commercially important and the fine matrix has preserved excellent impressions of numerous drifted land organisms - mainly plants, but also some insects - at several east Dorset localities. In Middle Eocene times, Bournemouth would have lain on the south-eastern edge of a tropical lowland margined by heaths, dunes, deltas and sandflats traversed by braided streams (Melville & Freshney, 1982). There were thus habitats nearby suitable for Odonata and *T. gossi* had a wingspan greater than that of any living British aeshnid which is consistent with a once warmer climate.

The Dorset fossils provide an important glimpse of the history of dragonflies because, with one possible exception, the species are unique to this area. Prospects for future discoveries are good. The liassic beds attract numerous fossil collectors every year and the

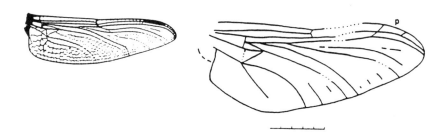

Figure 4. Fossil dragonfly wing (right). *Mesogomphus* sp., (Manchester Museum, LL10236) hind wing, Cypris Freestone, Lulworth Formation, showing main venation; p = pterostigma area. Scale line = mm. Left, wing of present day *Ictinogomphus* sp., from Africa, for comparison - not to scale.

chances of more Odonata being recovered are very high. The Lulworth Formation has yielded new finds in the last few years including wings from near Lulworth (Fig. 4) and the Isle of Portland (Coombefield and Inmosthay Quarries). Useful collecting in the Tertiary deposits is more difficult because of exploitation and deterioration of sections due to commercial activity, or simply the crumbly nature of these relatively young strata: surely, here is an opportunity for useful collaboration between naturalists, industrialists and civil engineers.

Acknowledgements

I am indebted to Dr. P.A. Selden (Manchester University) for bringing Mr Miller's find to my attention.

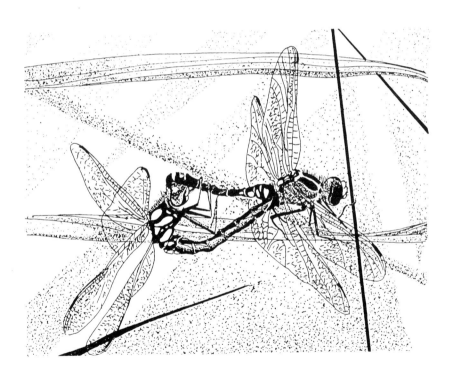

CHAPTER 5 - POND CONSTRUCTION FOR DRAGONFLIES -
British Dragonfly Society

Introduction

The decline in still-water habitats within the British Isles since the Second World War is all too obvious. Ponds provided by traditional farming methods to supply water for stock are usually no longer required, as piped supplies have been installed.

Redundant ponds, through natural succession, have dried out or have been deliberately filled in to provide additional land for agriculture or building. Often we see existing ponds used as refuse tips; or they may be simply neglected to become shaded out by trees and bushes.

Modern land-drainage techniques too have hastened the decline of our wetland habitats, either directly or indirectly, through the consequent lowering of the water table.

Although quantitative data are usually lacking, this loss of waterbodies has resulted in a serious reduction of dragonfly populations, along with those of other aquatic organisms, in many parts of Britain.

It is hoped that this paper will help to redress the balance by encouraging the construction of ponds.

Before considering some of the practical aspects of pond construction, we offer the following brief notes on the general habitat requirements of dragonflies.

General Habitat Requirements For British Dragonflies

1. All species depend on permanent water.

2. All species depend on both the condition (and stability) of their aquatic breeding site and the nature of the surrounding hinterland frequented by the adult (eg availability of feeding and roosting sites, etc.).

3. Warmth is essential; upland and northern areas generally have fewer species than lowland and southern regions. The best sites are those which are sunny and sheltered from the wind (particularly winds coming from the north and east).

4. An abundance of marginal, emergent and submerged aquatic vegetation is necessary for both adults and larvae. For adults such plants provide perching, roosting and oviposition sites. Submerged and emergent plants provide habitats for developing larvae while emergent plants are essential for emerging larvae. Newly emerged and immature adults require sheltered vegetation a few metres from water.

Notes on Renovation and Maintenance of Existing Ponds

Where practicable, it is sound conservation practice and often less expensive to renovate old ponds rather than create new ones. Plant and animal communities which have already become established can, through careful management, be modified and enhanced.

Populations of dragonflies should be monitored before and after management takes place in order to test its effectiveness.

Heavily silted and overgrown ponds should never be cleared completely in one operation. Autumn and winter are the best times and, if clearance is staged over a couple of years or more, natural recolonisation can take place. Unwanted plant growth should be removed carefully and with restraint. The use of herbicides is not recommended: decomposition of plants reduces the oxygen in water and may be detrimental to dragonflies and the other animals on which they depend for food.

Mechanical diggers are very convenient but should be used with care. It is easy to churn up pond margins and possibly cause damage to the bottom lining if one is present.

Heavily shaded ponds should be opened up to expose them to sunlight, either by selective removal of shrubs and trees or by careful pruning. Coppicing or pollarding may also be considered.

Farm ponds (unless they are very large) may receive too much manure from sheep and cattle. This source of increased nutrients should be reduced where possible. Pollution from slurry should be prevented.

Farm ponds may well be called upon as a supplementary source of water for irrigation or spraying in times of drought. Needless to say large fluctuations in water level should be avoided if possible. Measures should also be taken to prevent ponds from being damaged by traces of fertiliser and pesticides introduced when washing out spraying equipment or through spray drift.

Finally, if the site is to be used by others, especially children, consideration should be given to removing or shielding potential hazards such as deep water, steep banks etc.

Pond Construction

The following notes are for general information only and relate to the construction of small ponds in the garden environment or on the farm. Large-scale ventures are beyond the scope of this leaflet although, of course, the same basic principles would still apply.

Planning

The choice of site and the depth and outline of the pond are fundamental to success or failure.

The bigger the pond the better. Very small ponds support very few dragonflies. Most British species can breed in ponds of c. 14 square metres if the habitat is suitable.

The design of the pond should include the provision of shelter from prevailing winds, particularly those from the north and east. The pond should be sited away from overhanging trees for, not only may they shade out any proposed aquatic/marginal vegetation, but an excessive amount of autumn leaves pollute the water and can be a nuisance to clear out. Few dragonflies like shade!

Also avoid other possible sources of pollution (eg runoff from nearby roads or from intensively farmed land).

Establish the correct depth. Whilst shallow areas are important, a uniformly shallow pond will heat up in summer, reducing the oxygen level of the water and perhaps even dry out. Similarly, in winter it could freeze completely, killing much of the aquatic life you want to support; also the bottom lining may be damaged. It is important, therefore, to have a sufficient depth of water (eg 0.75-1.0m) at the deepest point.

The shape of the pond will depend upon individual circumstances but an irregular outline looks more natural and provides a longer edge. Vertical sides and sharp corners should if possible be avoided; shallow margins sloping gently down from the water's edge are important for the growth of floating and emergent plants and hence the larval habitat for the dragonflies you wish to encourage. Areas of shallow water should be considered for the southern and western aspects of the pond. By careful design it is possible to create a variety of habitats thereby encouraging a wider spectrum of dragonflies that may eventually breed in the pond.

Construction

Before marking out the proposed site check whether there are any underground services such as gas and water pipelines or telephone cables.

Pegs and string enable an accurate outline to be created and can easily be modified. It is a good idea to leave the outline marked out for several days before digging so that changes can be made. Is it in the correct position? If you propose to use a butyl-rubber liner, can you afford it at the amount required? If you propose to use a mechanical digger, can you get access? Before digging it is also worth considering where to put the waste soil. Perhaps you would like a rockery elsewhere in the garden. Or, if the site could do with some extra shelter, use the spoil to create a windbreak or bank (preferably facing south or south-west) on which adult dragonflies can bask while sheltered from the wind.

Whether the pond is dug manually or by machine the surface of the site should be level. If you are lucky enough to have a permanently high water table or if your garden is on impervious clay, a liner may not be necessary; but usually it is essential.

Pond liners are of three basic types:
1. Clay sealed.
2. Concrete
3. Membrane (rubber or plastic).

Before concrete and synthetic materials were available, puddled clay was the most common lining. However, this depends on the availability of suitable clay and involves a considerable amount of hard, skilled work; it has largely been superseded by the other methods.

Concrete lining tends to be difficult to install and requires a wire cage to support it. It is also prone to damage during a hard winter. The concrete needs to be applied skilfully and swiftly and must be prepared during good weather. It also needs to be waterproofed.

Repairs can be difficult.

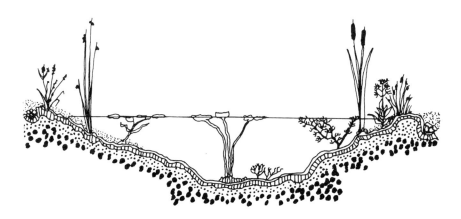

Figure 5. Cross section through pond to show distribution of aquatic plants and use of waterproof liner.

Creating a pond using a rubber/plastic lining

Thin membrane liners, such as butyl rubber and plastic, are extremely effective and relatively easy to install but are liable to be punctured. Used carefully this is the liner of choice for most ponds. Heavy-duty plastic however should be protected from strong sunlight which may damage it. 'Visqueen' polyethylene sheeting from ICI is a good material of this type but must be completely covered over to prevent deterioration.

When the pond has been excavated (and all sharp objects such as stone, twigs etc removed), the amount of lining required can be calculated. Remember to run the tape measure from the edge, down the side, along the bottom and up the other side. Allow for sufficient overlap beyond the pond margin (approx. 30-40 cm) as this is important for anchorage.

To provide a soft bed upon which to lay the lining, sifted sand or soil should be placed over the bottom of the pond.

This should then be covered with a layer of newspaper or, if available, old carpet for additional protection.

The lining is then stretched over the hole and gently adapted to the shape of the bottom and sides, pleating the creases as necessary. Anchor the edge of the lining with flattish rock slabs (these may be covered up later as required), or position the edge as indicated in the diagram, by folding it down into a narrow trench which is then filled with soil and covered with turves. Turves placed in a position slightly below the proposed water level make the edge look more natural.

Avoid pulling the lining taut. Similarly, allow extra slack to compensate for shrinkage on cooling after hot weather. For large ponds it may be necessary to join separate sheets of lining material to obtain the desired size. Advice should be sought from the manufacturer/supplier as to how this may best be achieved.

Filling

Water should be gradually introduced via a hose pipe until the pond is one half to three quarters full. This minimises disturbance to any bottom substrate you may have added and allows the lining to become stretched, so adapting it closely to the bottom.

Before completely filling the pond it is worth considering the possibility of punctures.

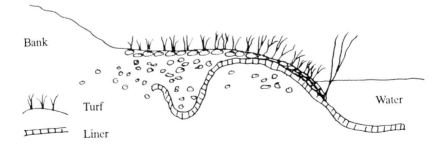

Figure 6. Diagram to show anchorage of liner to pond edge.

Some protection can be gained by fixing Hessian sacking or nylon mesh with sticky clay to potentially vulnerable areas of liner round the edge. Do not have too strong a current from the hose pipe when finally filling the pond as this will disturb the clay fixative.

When the pond is full the water should be allowed to stand for at least two days before plants or animals are introduced so as to allow the release of chlorine added during water treatment.

Developing the Pond

Planting

Late spring to early summer is the best time to establish aquatic plants. Warm water encourages growth.

Ideally, native species of submerged, floating and emergent plants should be chosen but, since no British species of dragonfly is dependent upon a particular species of plant during its lifecycle, this can be a matter of personal choice.

Many native plants can be readily bought or propagated from *cuttings* taken from a local watercourse. Always ask permission from the owner before removing any plant and make sure it is not a 'protected species'. Exercise moderation when collecting.

Rooted plants will of course require a bottom substrate, but since silting-up happens all too quickly, one may consider starting off with potted plants placed in the desired position. Open-mesh baskets, obtainable from a local garden centre, are ideal and allow unhindered growth as a natural substrate develops. Potted plants can also be raised up on house bricks if the water is too deep in the chosen position. Once a substrate has formed, further plant

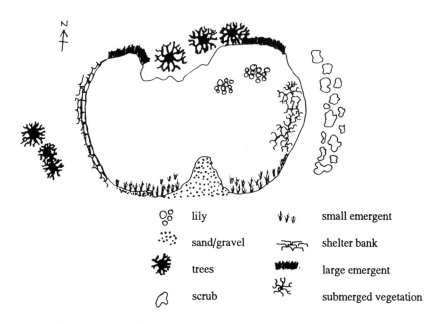

⚬	lily	↓↓↓	small emergent
∴	sand/gravel		shelter bank
✳	trees		large emergent
⌒	scrub		submerged vegetation

Figure 7. Plan of pond to show distribution of aquatic and fringing vegetation.

cuttings may be inserted directly, weighted down with a stone until they root.

Although organisms rapidly colonise newly created ponds, a bucket or two of water and substrate from a well established pond will introduce smaller animal life, snail's eggs etc. It is inadvisable to keep fish or wildfowl in a pond designed for dragonflies. They may eat your dragonfly larvae and can be a potential source of pollution.

Suggested plants:-

Deeper water -Submerged Plants.
Curly Pondweed (*Potamogeton crispus*)
Water Starwort (*Callitriche* spp.)
Hornwort (*Ceratophyllum demersum*)
Spiked Water Milfoil (*Myriophyllum spicatum*)
Canadian Pondweed (*Elodea canadensis*) but it may be difficult to control.

Deeper water Floating Plants
Stiff-leaved Water Crowfoot (*Ranunculus circinatus*)
Frogbit (*Hydrocharis morsus-ranae*)
Broad-leaved Pondweed (*Potamogeton natans*)
Amphibious Bistort (*Polygonum amphibium*)
White Water-lily (*Nymphaea alba*)
Yellow Water-lily (*Nuphar lutea*)
Fringed Water-lily (*Nymphoides peltata*)

Shallow water Emergent Plants

Flowering Rush (*Butomus umbellatus*)
Water Horsetail (*Equisetum fluviatile*)
Bur-reed (*Sparganium erectum*)
Water Plantain (*Alisma plantago-aquatica*)
Common Spike-rush (*Eleocharis palustris*)
Reed Mace (*Typha latifolia*) but it may be difficult to control
Bog bean (*Menyanthes trifoliata*)

Avoid Common Reed (*Phragmites australis*) and New Zealand Water Stonecrop (*Crassula helmsii*) as these rapidly spread and can be difficult to control.

Algal Blooms
Until the water community becomes a balanced system, a common phenomenon with recently created ponds at spring time is the algal bloom, the water taking on the colour and consistency of turbid coffee or pea soup. Although intractable cases do occur, the problem should ultimately sort itself out. Shade and competition provided by floating and submerged plants, and the microscopic grazing animals which they support, should provide a natural control. Do not use chemical preparations.

Pond Maintenance
Unwanted invasive plants should be thinned out in autumn. Water-lilies can be particularly troublesome. In excess they can lower the water level through transpiration and

the strong rhizomes/roots can be difficult to remove.

Silt and leaf-litter should be controlled but since they provide important habitat for bottom-dwelling larvae the rule is not to be over-zealous. Remove a little at a time!

During warm weather top up the water level regularly. Large quantities of cold chlorinated tap water added suddenly may be detrimental, so it is best to add water in small instalments.

Colonisation

The rate at which a new pond becomes colonised by dragonflies depends mainly on the distance between the pond and other waterbodies supporting dragonfly populations. Most dragonflies are efficient dispersers and they find new habitats very quickly. Experience shows that new ponds rapidly become colonised if there are dragonflies breeding within two or three miles of them.

New ponds take some time to mature and, although they may be visited by many species quite soon after construction, it may take a few years before the visitors actually breed successfully in them.

In southern England the following species are known to frequently colonise garden ponds:-

Azure Damselfly *Coenagrion puella*
Blue-tailed Damselfly *Ischnura elegans*
Southern Hawker *Aeshna cyanea*
Broad-bodied Chaser *Libellula depressa*
Common Darter *Sympetrum striolatum*

FURTHER READING

BIOLOGY AND CONSERVATION

Corbet, P.S., (1962) 1983. *A Biology of Dragonflies* Classey Reprint

Corbet, P.S., Longfield, C. and Moore, N.W., (1960) 1985. *Dragonflies* Collins New Naturalist

Chelmick, David; Hammond, Cyril; Moore, Norman, and Stubbs, Alan, 1980. *The Conservation of Dragonflies* Nature Conservancy Council

Miller, P.L., 1987. *Dragonflies* Naturalists' Handbooks 7. Cambridge University Press

Identification Guides

Askew, R.R., 1988 *The Dragonflies of Europe* Harley

d'Aguilar, J., Dommanget, J-L., and Préchac, R., 1986. *A Field Guide to the Dragonflies of Britain, Europe and North Africa*. Collins

Gibbons, Bob, 1986 *Guide to the Dragonflies and Damselflies of Britain and Northern Europe*. Country Life

Hammond, C.O., (1977) 1983. *Dragonflies of Great Britain and Ireland*. 2nd edn. (revised by R. Merritt). Harley

McGeeney, A., 1986. *A Complete Guide to British Dragonflies* Jonathan Cape

Welstead, Noelle and Tony, 1984. *The Dragonflies of the New Forest* Hampshire and Isle of Wight Naturalists Trust

REFERENCES

Chapters 1 and 2

Barnes, L.E., 1983 'The colonization of ball-clay ponds by macroinvertebrates and macrophytes', *Freshwater Biology* 13:561-578.

Brown, S.C.S., 1988 'The Lost Dragonfly of Dorset', *Newsletter* Jan: 11. Dorset Trust for Nature Conservation.

Corbet 1983; Corbet, Longfield and Moore 1985; and Miller 1987 - see above.

Friday, L.E., 1987 'The diversity of macroinvertebrate and macrophyte communities in ponds', *Freshwater Biology* 18:87-104.

Friday, L.E., 1988 'The conservation and amenity value of ball-clay ponds in the Isle of Purbeck', *Biological Conservation* 43:165-168.

Moore, N.W., 1964 'Intra- and interspecific competition among dragonflies (Odonata). An account of observations and field experiments on population density control in Dorset, 1954-60' *J. Anim. Ecol.* 33:49-71.

Moore, N.W., 1991 'The Last of *Oxygastra curtisi* (Dale) in England?' *J. Br. Dragonfly Soc.* 7:6-10.

Chapter 4.

Allen, P., 1976 'Wealden of the Weald : a new model'. *Proceedings of the Geologists' Association*, London, **86** (4) : 389-437.

Asahina, S., 1954 *A morphological study of a relic dragonfly Epiophlebia superstes Selys (Odonata, Anisozygoptera)* iv + 153 pp., 71 pls. Japan Society for the Promotion of Science, Tokyo.

Campion, H., 1916 *Triaeschna gossi*, a new genus and species of Odonata from the Eocene of Bournemouth. *Annals and Magazine of Natural History* (8) **18** : 229-234, pl. XI.

Carle, F.L., 1982 'The wing venation homologies and phylogeny of the Odonata: a continuing debate'. *Societas Internationais Odonatologica Rapid Communications,* Utrecht, **4** : 1-66.

Daley, B., & Crewdson, P., 1987 'Bournemouth Cliffs'; a revised cliff profile and an account of the present distribution of exposures', *Tertiary Research,* London, **8** (4) : 127-132.

Handlirsch, A., 1906-08 *Die fossilen Insekten und die Phylogenie der Rezenten Formen.* ix + 1430 pp. Engelmann, Leipzig.

Handlirsch, A., 1939 'Neue Untersuchungen über die fossilen Insekten 2. Teil, *Annalen des Naturhistorischen Museums,* Wien, **49** : 1-240, pls. 1-16.

Harland, W.B., Cox, A.V., Llewellyn, P.G., Pickton, C.A.G., Smith, A.G., & Walters, R., 1982 *A geological time scale.* 131 pp. Cambridge University Press.

Jarzembowski, E.A., 1987 Early Cretaceous insects from southern England. Ph.D. thesis (unpublished), University of Reading.

Melville, R.V., & Freshney, E.C., 1982 The Hampshire Basin and adjoining areas (4th ed.). *British Regional Geology,* London, viii + 146 pp.

Pritykina, L.N., 1980 Otryad Libellulida. *In:* Rodendorf, B.B. (ed.) *Istoricheskoe razvitie klassa nasekomykh.* Trudy Paleontologicheskogo Instituta, Moskva, Leningrad, **175** : 128-134, figs 67-9.

Sladen, C.P., & Batten, D.J., 1984 'Source-area environment of late Jurassic and early Cretaceous sediments in south-east England,' *Proceedings of the Geologists' Association,* London, **95** (2) : 149-163.

Townson, W.G., 1975 'Lithostratigraphy and deposition of the type Portlandian' *Journal of the Geological Society, London,* **131**: 619-638.

Westwood, J.O., 1854 'Contributions to fossil entomology', *Quarterly Journal of the Geological Society of London,* **10**: 378-396, pls. 14-18.

Whalley, P.E.S., 1985 'Systematics and palaeogeography of the Lower Jurassic insects of Dorset, England', *Bulletin of the British Museum (Natural History),* London (Geology) **39** (3): 107-189.

Zeuner, F.E., 1962 'Fossil insects from the Lower Lias of Charmouth, Dorset,' *Bulletin of the British Museum (Natural History),* London (Geology) **7** (5) : 153-171, pls. 24-7.

Chapter 5.

British Trust for Conservation, *Waterways and Wetlands* Volunteers Handbook

Clegg, J. 1965 *Freshwater Life* Warne

Fitter, R., and Manuel, R., 1986. *Field Guide to Freshwater Life.* Collins

Kabisch, K., and Hammerling, J., 1984. *Pools and Ponds - Oases in the Countryside.* Croom Helm

Nature Conservancy Council 1980. *Farm Ponds* Countryside Conservation Handbook. Leaflet No. 5.

Thompson, B., and Coldrey, J., 1985. *The Pond* Collins

Acknowledgements

I am grateful to the many people who have contributed to this publication, especially to Dr Norman Moore and Dr Ed Jarzembowski for their accounts of dragonflies, present and past. Dr Moore, in addition, kindly read the text and made valuable comments, which led to amendments. Richard Surry, Keeper of Records, Dorset Environmental Records Centre, prepared the maps and helped in many other ways. Noelle and Tony Welstead have most generously allowed the reproduction from their *Dragonflies of the New Forest* 1984 of the drawings on p. 8 and all the illustrations which accompany the species accounts, with the exception of the Scarce Chaser on p. 48 and those on pp. 51 and 55. These and fig. 2 are by Aïda O'Sullivan. The Banded Demoiselle at fig. 3 was drawn by Tracey Roberts, whilst Debbie Maidment drew the vignettes on the front cover and on pp. 21, 62 and 72. Dr N.R. Webb and Messrs J.R. Cox, David Pearman and B.P. Pickess were prominent among others who have given their help. Map 2 is based, by permission, on a map in *The Butterflies of Dorset* 1984 (J. Thomas and N. Webb). The chapters on the Code of Practice when collecting dragonflies, and Pond Construction for Dragonflies, are reproduced by courtesy of the British Dragonfly Society.

Without generous grants from the English China Clay Company (ECC) and Wessex Water, and a loan from the Saffron Cleaning Company, it is unlikely that this publication would have appeared. The editorial assistance of Jo Draper has been vital. Christopher Chaplin skilfully dealt with the lettering of the maps and diagrams.

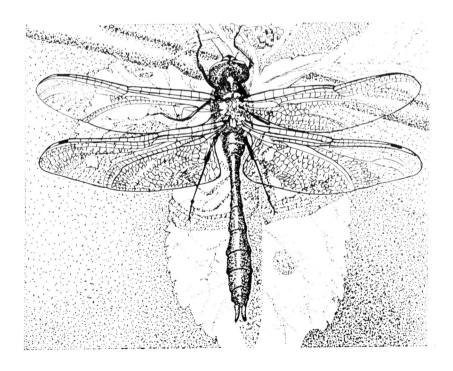

Index of Species

The bold figure indicates the species account